TOM SLOANE — MASTER MARINER

Tom Sloane – Master Mariner

CAPTAIN R. C. PROCTOR OBE

Copyright © R. C. Proctor, 2002

First published in 2002 on behalf of the author
by Scotforth Books,
Carnegie House,
Chatsworth Road,
Lancaster LA1 4SL,
England
Tel: +44(0)1524 840111
Fax: +44(0)1524 840222
email: carnegie@provider.co.uk
Publishing and book sales: www.carnegiepub.co.uk
Book production: www.wooof.net

British Library Cataloguing-in-Publication data
A catalogue record for this book is available from the British Library

ISBN 1-904244-04-1

Typeset in Bell 11 on 13
by Carnegie Publishing
Printed and bound in the UK
by Bookcraft (Bath) Ltd

To my four grandsons,
Charles, James, Timothy and David Proctor

Captain R. C. Proctor OBE

Illustrations

Introduction

THIS IS A FASCINATING STORY of faraway places, from the cold of northern Canada to the heat of the tropics and as far south as New Zealand. It is a tale of weird cargoes, labour disputes and conditions on early ships and is based on the experiences of the author but told through the character of Tom Sloane, a master mariner.

Robert Campbell Proctor was born in Sunderland in 1899 and was the eldest of three boys and four girls. He served with the British Merchant Navy and was apprenticed to the Prince Line in 1913 when just fifteen years old. The shipping firm, owned by the late Sir James Knott, was based in Newcastle and engaged in world wide trade. The Prince Line ships were distinguished by two red painted bands round the funnel and by the white Prince of Wales feathers on either side. The company is sadly no longer in existance and most of the shipping was sold some years ago.

Captain Proctor served his apprenticeship during the First World War, after which he was away from home most of the time taking contracts that could last for up to three years. During this time he came to know Battery Park in New York, Nova Scotia and Hong Kong better than he knew Tyneside, the result being that his family knows little about him. He continued to work with the company for fifty years, the sea and ships becoming the love of his life, and showing himself to be a dedicated, resourceful and confident seaman who never doubted his own abilities.

He was awarded the Order of the British Empire during the Second World War for service to the country above and beyond the call of duty when his ship was blown up in the Mediterranean. He was carrying military supplies to Calcutta for the British Army under General Slim in the Burma campaign against the Japanese.

In later years he was a freemason and a member of an antiquarian society who had an enthusiasm for geography, occasionally lecturing on places visited during his career.

Captain Proctor passed away in 1986 and this volume is being published posthumously in his memory by his son, Robert S. Proctor.

Chapter 1

CAPTAIN TOM SLOANE OBE was now seventy-two years of age and had been enjoying retirement for the past seven years. A quiet man, softly spoken, about five feet eight inches tall and sturdily built, with a good head of silvery grey hair, he had the blue eyes of a man of the sea, with a thoughtful look at all times, as if thinking of the past fifty years of his life in the service of the Prince Line shipping company, during which time he rose from apprentice boy to Master.

From 1913 to 1963, he was trading to most of the known ports of the world in both hemispheres and a man cannot lightly let such years slip into the forgotten past.

He had had a full life, with every day a challenge. For half of his life he had worked through the various grades of officership and for the other half he had been master of many ships.

Tom's forebears were mariners serving in the East India Company and the China tea clippers. One was known to have been a French prisoner of war from one of His Majesty's ships during the Napoleonic wars as he turned up seven years after the war ended more a Frenchman than English, much to the astonishment of his relatives who had had no idea of his whereabouts.

During the seven years of Captain Tom's retirement seafaring had altered considerably. Ships were being built of over two hundred thousand tons deadweight, mostly oil tankers, but dry cargoes were now shipped in containers of twenty to forty tons weight, these containers being loaded at the factories, then transported to the ship, where they were loaded by special cranes and stowed in their entirety, so as not to be disturbed before arriving at their destination.

When Tom reached the age of fourteen, he left school with an excellent report from his teacher. He lived within the sound of ships of all sizes being built on the river Tyne. First, it would be the tramp, tramp of boots on the road, whole armies of men going to their work in the shipyards about 5.30 a.m. from Monday to Saturday, then the rhythmic hammering of rivets being knocked home on the steel hulls of future ships.

He sat on his father's shoulders to see the launch of the famous *Mauretania* and saw the same ship pass out between the Tyne piers as a completed vessel, one of the wonders of shipbuilding in those days. Indeed, many ships, both warships and merchant ships, were born on the river Tyne, and ships were forever going and coming.

Coal was the main export from the river, and on the banks were wooden structures called staiths where wagon-loads of coal were poured into ships' holds. Ships would be lying off in tiers waiting for their turn to load. The work went on at all the staiths through day and night, but Sunday was always a quiet day when many people walked along the river banks to see the ships. A very busy river indeed.

Tom's parents realised that he desired to make shipping his career, so his mother took him to Newcastle to visit the shipping offices. Ships of all classes were available for apprentices on a ten pound surety, ships that were in the tramping trade, so it came to pass that Tom was presented to the Prince Line, whose owner was Mr James Knott.

They were interviewed by a very overpowering gentleman with a white beard, Captain Willis, who asked questions of Tom's mother as to whether her boy was in good health and could work hard, at the same time looking at the said boy as if he were up for sale and he was wanting a good bargain. They were dismissed with the promise that they would hear from the company in due course, and after a month or so a letter came from the Prince Line in which was enclosed a set of indentures which had to be signed by his parents and a witness. This matter was attended to, and Tom was told he would be joining a new ship, SS *Tuscan Prince*, just completing at Doxford's shipyard, Sunderland. The ship had to come to the Tyne for bunker coal, so he joined her at the coaling staiths at North Shields.

Previous to joining, Tom had to be fitted out with suitable clothes, also an apprentice's uniform for which the company supplied a cap badge and brass buttons. The indentures were for four years, and for that time he would receive forty pounds, made up of eight, nine, ten and thirteen pounds annually with one shilling a month for washing, and for this he was to be taught the duties of a seaman. Tom never gave the conditions a second thought, and just got on with the new way of life.

When the time came for Tom to leave home to join his ship, his parents, sisters and brother realised they were parting, which made him wonder whether he was wise to be leaving home. But off he went with his bag on his shoulder, and soon he was whistling on his way.

There at the coaling staiths he saw his brand-new ship lying at the tiers for the next ship to bunker. She looked a picture, all newly painted, straight from the shipyard, which was much better than joining some old tub full of cockroaches and rats, as could have been the case.

A man in a small boat was ferrying people to the ship, so Tom hailed it in his boyish voice. He jumped in with his bag and was soon at the bottom end of a rope ladder which he climbed with difficulty and fell over the bulwarks on to the deck.

He had arrived in his new world.

Chapter 2

A FTER HE HAD SURVEYED all that was to be seen in his immediate focus, Tom thought he had indeed stepped into a wonderful new world.

A young boy of his own age, seeing him looking about with such interest, came over, and in a kindly Irish brogue asked if he could help him. The offer was taken, and so he was introduced to the apprentices' accommodation amidships. The Irish lad was the engineers' messroom steward, and from that moment they set up a friendship which lasted over twenty years, by which time Tom was Chief Officer and the Irish lad Chief Steward.

Soon the Chief Officer appeared and Tom introduced himself. The Chief Officer, a kindly man, spoke to him like a father, giving him instructions on his new life and how to adjust himself to ship life and his new quarters. He was also informed that three other boys were joining, all new like himself. One was coming from London, one from Lincoln and the other from South Shields, so it would be late in the day before they arrived.

Eventually they joined, bunks were selected and bags and sea chests stowed away after keeping out the working clothes for immediate use. All had a meal in their messroom, after bringing the food from the galley, then the Chief Officer brought in a list of routine jobs for the purpose of keeping their quarters clean. Each boy had to take his turn to scrub out the room every morning from 6 to 8 a.m. and clean all the brasswork (and there was plenty) – brass door handles, finger plates, doorstep, lamps and hand grips for the drawers, all of which he would personally inspect. The Bosun would take care of the other three boys as to their work.

Next day all the crew appeared at the Mercantile Marine Office at North Shields, together with Tom and his fellow apprentices, for the purpose of signing the agreement. The apprentices had time to survey all the members of the crew on this occasion, and saw that there were about forty of them. The Shipping Master, as he was called, spent some time reading out the agreement, then asked if all were satisfied. On being informed that they were, he proceeded to take their signatures alongside their rating. Pay for a seaman was then three pounds per month, with the firemen ten shillings extra, paid in gold. Apprentices had only to give their particulars to the Shipping Master, which he wrote in the back of the agreement, also examining their indentures. The Third Officer, who was in charge of them, then took them to the Shipping Federation, where they received a blue form each to indicate that they were members of the Federation.

After these formalities, they all returned to the ship and found she was under the coal tips, and coal was being poured into the bunkers in wagon-loads. Tom found his father and mother, with his young brother, on board awaiting him, and needless to say, he was delighted to see them. The Chief Officer was good enough to show them all around the ship, and they must have been very well satisfied with all they saw. But that could not stop the tears in his mother's eyes, much as she tried to conceal them.

The ship sailed on 11 December, and when passing Lloyd's Hailing Station near the mouth of the river, a voice came over the water, asking, 'What ship and where bound?' to be answered by a sonorous voice from the bridge – 'Middlesbrough, Antwerp, London and the Plate', meaning, of course, the River Plate in the Argentine.

Middlesbrough, the first stop for loading cargo, was only a stay of two days, but the father of one of the apprentices, Paul, went there to see him: a fine gentleman who took them all to a very nice meal at a restaurant.

The next port was Antwerp – Tom's very first foreign port. Being winter everything was covered with snow, and much colder than England. The Seamen's Mission padre came on board and soon made himself known to all, inviting everyone to the special Christmas dinner to be held at the Mission. Christmas Day was spent at Antwerp while cargo was being loaded. Somehow, working at night did not seem to be the thing. Perhaps it was because the lighting was inadequate as only carbon lamps were used on deck, that is two sticks of carbon touching each other, which made a rather good light. There were no fixed lights in the holds.

What a dinner they all had at the Mission – all the crew were there, sailors, firemen, stewards and the apprentices. British ladies were waiting at table, and every morsel that should be at a Christmas dinner was there, all washed down with plenty of soft drinks. There was a party afterwards, which made everyone merry and bright, and Tom thought this was an excellent life. It was Christmas 1913.

The *Tuscan Prince* left Antwerp shortly afterwards for London, and docked at 'E' jetty, Victoria Docks, apparently a berth which the company always used. In those days Grace Company were the ship's agents.

Night work was done here, all the lighting gear being supplied from the shore. The ship used oil lamps for the crew's accommodation, and a special rating called the lamp trimmer was employed to trim the lamps of all the rooms and crew's quarters and replenish the paraffin oil.

Eventually the ship left London fully loaded, with two huge barges over No. 4 and 5 hatches, which were aft. The ship steamed down the Thames, dropped the river pilot off Gravesend and continued out around North

Foreland, past Dover, and so along the English Channel, discharging the North Sea Pilot at Brixham. It was not until then that Captain Burgess joined the ship.

So the *Tuscan Prince* sailed away to warmer climates, and Tom and the other first trippers were beginning to find their way about, but kept no watches yet. The Bosun was a kindly old salt and kept them working, helping him or the storekeeper, while sometimes the carpenter needed them to steady up the planks he was making into spare hatches. Helping the lamp trimmer meant cleaning the glasses of the lamps or bringing them all on deck for better trimming. There was always the wheel-house and the chart-room to scrub out. All the brasswork had to be polished between 6 and 8 a.m. – the telegraphs to the engine room, the bells on the forecastle head and the bridge, including the crows' nest, and the brass around the portholes, which was about two inches wide, all had to shine with elbow grease and polish.

Decks were scraped and painted with red lead, the weather being fine after leaving the Bay of Biscay. They all felt squeamish and sick in the Bay, but that soon passed. They relished their food, but the tea tasted awful. It was made in a big boiler and stewed till it tasted like dishwater.

Many sailing ships were seen backing and filling in the doldrums. Flag signals would go up when close enough to be seen, stating ships' names and where bound and from which port, and all this information would be entered in the Scrap Log by the Officer of the Watch.

Ships did not carry wireless telegraphy in those days, so they would report to ships whenever possible. Most headlands all over the world had Lloyd's Signal Stations, and whenever possible ships would report in passing with hoists of flags in the International Code, and this would be telegraphed to London.

One of the first subjects Tom and his buddies had to learn was the International Code of Signals, together with the International Code Book, and later came semaphore and the morse alphabet.

In due course the ship arrived at Montevideo, at the entrance to the River Plate, calling there for a day or so to discharge some cargo, then off to Buenos Aires, about a hundred miles up the river. At its mouth the river was so wide that one could not see the other side, but the water was brownish in colour, and fresh. This fresh water was good for washing down the ship. Further up-river it was even good for drinking purposes.

On arriving at Buenos Aires, the sailors wore jerseys with the company's name in white across the chest, and sailor hats with the ship's name on. Tom and his pals wore their uniforms, one boy forward with the Chief Officer, one aft with the Second Officer, and the other two handy for passing messages from each end to the bridge. The first thing they did with their uniform caps was to knock them out of shape until there was no stiffness left, then they would be ready to wear, perched on the back of the head. This was only while the ship was passing through the locks into the dock, for when the ship was tied up off came the finery and it was down to work again. This was no doubt to make an impression, being a new ship, upon all and sundry. About three or four ships of the company were in the docks, and soon many visitors were arriving on board, not forgetting the apprentices. Tom knew he and his fellow apprentices were not to stay long on this ship, as the company had a regular trade between New York and South America, and some of the apprentices would be due to go home, which the *Tuscan Prince* intended to do shortly.

One gentleman who was aboard early was the padre from the Seamen's Mission. Carny was his name, and he was a man of wide experience, having spent some time at the San Francisco Mission, and he was known as 'The Fighting Parson', apparently through his dealings with the sailors' boarding houses. He encouraged Tom and his shipmates to visit the Mission, and as one of the main attractions there was the boxing ring he soon had them all under instruction. He claimed that the 'noble art' was a necessity when trading in South American ports.

There were other attractions at the Mission, such as social nights when girl hostesses were invited for dancing. Buenos Aires had quite a large British population, working on the railways and in shipping and farming. The hostesses were all British girls, and a grand crowd they were.

All the other apprentices in the port attended the Mission, as usually their financial allowance did not allow them to go anywhere else. Boys from sailing ships and steamships mixed freely, and often had heated differences of opinion on the merits of their training, sail or steam. The padre would watch out for any trouble and would soon have the differences settled in the ring, with cheering apprentices supporting their particular fancy. The padre was a grand man and would stand no nonsense, which was good for Tom and his shipmates, who were young and new to it all.

In due course the ship was discharged of her cargo, including the two barges, and proceeded to Rosario, up-river about thirty hours' steaming. Rosario was a small place compared to Buenos Aires, but there was an off-shoot of a Mission run by a lay preacher. Although Tom did not experience such a boisterous time as at the last port it was a good place to go to and meet people.

Eventually all the cargo from Europe was discharged, and the ship was made ready to take a grain cargo in bulk. Only part of the cargo was taken at Rosario, as the waters were too shallow to take a full cargo. The ship would complete loading at Buenos Aires, the cargo being for Santos in Brazil.

SS *Portuguese Prince.*

After leaving Buenos Aires the ship proceeded on its way to Santos, a matter of about four days' steaming. On arrival, one of the company's vessels, SS *Portuguese Prince*, was already there.

This was the time for Tom and his fellow apprentices to move over to this other ship.

The *Portuguese Prince* was only two years old, and three apprentices had completed their indentures, having been two years away from home. The *Portuguese Prince* must have been waiting to make this exchange, as she sailed without any further ado for Rio de Janeiro. The remaining apprentice was soon taking charge of the new boys. His name was Olivier and he had two years time in.

Rio de Janeiro was surrounded by magnificent scenery, and Tom found it breathtaking. Huge mountains all around rose to tremendous peaks, and on one of these peaks stood the statue of Christ which must have been a tremendous size as it could be so plainly seen.

The *Portuguese Prince* anchored in a bay protected from all the winds, with the city lying at the foot of the mountains. The ship loaded her cargo from barges, so that work could carry on over both sides. Hides were in the deep tanks, so that the smell could be sealed from the clean cargo.

The next port was Victoria, about two or three days up the coast. There the ship passed through a narrow channel and into a wider expanse of water. More or less the same type of cargo was loaded here as at the previous port.

Off again, this time to Bahia, another few days' steaming, and there picked up cargo of a similar nature. The apprentices were kept very busy laying dunnage wood and rush mats so that the cargo would not touch the steel in the 'tween decks. The dunnage, laid grating fashion, allowed a circulation of air under the bags of coffee and similar cargo; otherwise such cargoes could soon be contaminated with mould. The officers did their own tallying of the cargo, as they got a percentage of the freight as bonus at the end of the voyage, but any damage had to be covered by that bonus. The officers were expected to stay two years on the ship before being relieved and sent home, while the apprentices could go on until their indentures were completed.

The next port of call was Recife or Pernambuco. An outside reef guarded this harbour like a natural breakwater.

More bags of coffee beans were loaded, together with boxes of raw rubber and other commodities of a vegetable nature. When loading was finished, the ship sailed for Trinidad in the West Indies for bunker coal.

Although Tom worked hard, he began to think that he must study hard too, all through his apprenticeship. At present he had no books for that purpose and the possibility was that half of his apprenticeship would be over before he was in the UK again. He needed text books to give him a start, so he made up his mind to consult the Seamen's Mission padre in New York, where his ship was eventually bound.

All the sailors and engine room ratings were Germans, about thirty altogether, while the cooks and stewards were full-blooded coloured people. The ship apparently took all her crew from New York. The Chief Officer was a strong disciplinarian, being a man of middle age. The Captain was very rarely seen. That there should be young apprentices on board did not seem to interest him.

The ship called at Trinidad, took her bunker coal aboard and proceeded to New Orleans, which is on the Mississippi delta, several miles inland, with low swampy land on each side of the waterway. Before reaching New Orleans the ship had to be fumigated, with all the cargo on board, at the quarantine station about three miles below the city.

The place was infested with mosquitoes, which played the very devil with all on board, especially fresh young apprentices. Fumigation took about six hours, after which the ship proceeded to the city, tying up at the foot of Canal Street. The river boats, the big stern-wheelers with their steam organs, were berthed ahead of the ship.

Tom found the mosquitoes bad at night-time. The ship also had to be moved off the wharf-side at night to keep the rats off.

The ship did not stop long at this port. All the discharging was done by Negro labourers who were always chanting and singing quaint tunes, and Tom wondered whether many professional singers and bands had started from the New Orleans wharves.

Jack Johnson, the world heavyweight champion, fought his last fight, with the Texan cowboy, Jess Willard, somewhere in this area. Johnson had to lie down for the count as the probability was that he would have been shot if he hadn't. The 'white trash' spent a riotous time chasing the coloured people out of their homes to celebrate the victory of the Texan.

Paul and Tom were soon ashore to see the city lights, and on the road up they saw a new mode of transport, the Jetney 'bus, driven by the internal combustion engine. Merely a few wooden seats on the frame of a model 'T' Ford car, it carried about six people to town at ten cents a time.

The ship left New Orleans for New York with part of the cargo for that port. All this was new to the boys except Olivier. Nevertheless Tom and the two other rookies were taking everything in their stride. The sea life was agreeing with them, the food was good and although the work was hard to boys unaccustomed to it, they were gradually getting into good shape; in fact, they were growing up fast, physically and mentally. The Chief Officer had them taking turns at steering the ship in the dog watches, and they were gaining confidence every day. The ship had wooden decks, and they would discard their boots and run about in their bare feet in the warm sunny weather.

In due course the *Portuguese Prince* arrived at New York; not the New York of today, but at the end of the last decade before the First World War. So no extraordinary buildings met their gaze on Manhattan Island, the highest building being the World Building with a golden dome. It cannot be found now, as it is just a shrimp of a building compared with those of today. Brooklyn was all green fields, and all signs of dwelling houses stopped at Morse's Dry Docks, which are now Bethlehem Steel.

The ship berthed at Pier 4, Bush Terminal, Brooklyn. This was a long jetty jutting out into the bay. It was about half a mile long and a couple of hundred yards wide, all made of wood and completely enclosed by roof and sides, with huge doors which slung up inside, leaving a clear landing for merchandise from the ships. Three ships could be accommodated on each side of this pier. The Swedish-American immigrant ships used the outside berths at the bottom of the pier to land their emigrants from Europe. Such traffic used a gangway close up to the roof, so that they did not interfere with the working of other ships.

Tom found plenty of life here. Generally one or two other ships of the Prince Line were lying at berths on either side, perhaps one loading for the east coast of South America and another discharging from South African ports, and maybe another discharging from the Far East. The smells of

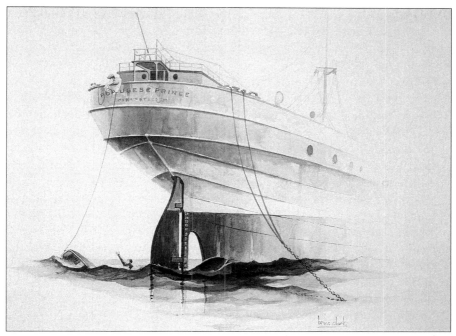

A painting of SS *Portuguese Prince* by Bruce Clark.

such cargoes were most enchanting, as they came from produce from all over the world; smells that Tom remembered all his life as they were associated with all the cargoes he had to deal with during his long career with the company.

The company's Superintendent had an office down about the middle of the dock, together with the Stores Superintendent. They attended to all the ship's requirements, while agents in New York saw to the cargoes.

When the cargo was out, the ship was dry-docked for a day or so at Morse's floating dock in order to clean and paint the ship's bottom. The crew were paid off on arrival, and re-signed when wanted again. No emigration laws troubled anybody in those days as such laws did not come into being until 1925. Often apprentices deserted their ships, and soon found employment ashore. Sometimes they came back after a month or so – that is, if they were accepted back.

Tom remarked on a fine ship lying up at the lay-by berth at Morse's Dry Docks. She was called the *Scot* and was owned by an American. He found out she was built for the South African trade by the Union Mail Line of Great Britain.

The 'Flying Angel' Seamen's Mission, which was situated in South

Street, The Battery, Manhattan, was one of the highlights of entertainment for the apprentices, and all the lads would gather there on certain nights of the week, particularly Thursday night, as that was dancing night with British girls.

Sunday was usually a quiet day in port. In the afternoon, a great worker for the welfare of British seamen, particularly apprentices, Mr William Wood, would arrive with his own steam launch, complete with a captain and a chief engineer. He would collect all the apprentices in port from the ships at anchor and alongside, probably picking up about thirty of them, with all kinds of badges in their caps, being of different companies, and take them all to St John's Church at the Battery, nearly down to the water front. In fact, the boat could sail right into a wharf which led to the church door.

They would all attend the 6 p.m. service which was open to everyone, the church being Anglican. The parson was the one that attended the Seamen's Mission, and after the service there would be tea for all the boys, attended by one or two elderly ladies. The boys made their own tea, then, lashed into all the goodies provided, then they were all shipped back to their ships after an enjoyable time.

Billy Wood was a great man, and along with his wife did a lot of good work for the boys. Many times, when the boys met each other in foreign ports, they would recall with pleasure the good work he did.

As this was Tom's first time in New York he was very impressed with all he saw. He and Paul, with only one dollar in their pockets, visited Coney Island and were quite taken with the way the younger people enjoyed themselves on the various activities. Food was cheap, and a big ham sandwich or a hamburger would only cost a few cents. There was an ice-cream shop kept by an old lady and her daughter along 3rd Avenue, Brooklyn, just a few minutes' walk from the ship. They were very kind to apprentices and supplied ice-cream on tick until one could pay for same. It was known as Mother Mary's shop, and most of the apprentices called there. The ice-cream was wonderful – the real stuff.

The ship eventually sailed for Santos, Brazil, after calling in at Rio on the way down. Santos was a typical South American port, and had been a bad place for malaria owing to the terrible mosquito. At that time the United States were shipping huge drainage pipes to drain all the refuse away to the sea, and these were in the process of being laid.

A lot of the pipes would be left on the quayside until wanted, and an army of men, deserters off ships, made these their hide-out and were a menace to all, always cadging for money to buy the local drink, casash, which was pure spirit from the sugar cane. They had reached about the lowest level a man could reach. They were men of all nations, and it is said that when the war started these men were all shipped away somewhere, but just where was very vague.

Santos was not an attractive port in those days. Nevertheless the cargo the ship took there all helped to make it one of the healthiest ports of the Continent.

Coffee in bags was shipped for the United States again, and the ship proceeded back on the same run as before. The *Portuguese Prince* arrived back in New York about the beginning of July 1914 and left at the end of the month with a full cargo consisting of all the steelwork of an abattoir and freezing plant for La Plata near Buenos Aires.

The crew were as before all German ratings in the engine room and on deck, including the petty officers. The ship went to Newport News for bunker coal, and while they were there, war was declared between Germany and Great Britain. The crew went along with the ship as before, however, as nobody saw any reason for a change, and the *Portuguese Prince* sailed from Newport News for La Plata with British officers and a German crew of able-bodied seamen. When off Pernambuco, well out of sight of land, at about 10 p.m., one day, a warship overtaking them signalled by morse lamp, asking the usual request: 'What ship and where bound?' The Third Officer was reading the signal with much difficulty, and Tom was doing his best to take it down with the bullseye lantern for light. When the message was answered with the name of the ship and port bound to, the warship came back with 'Warship *Good Hope*. Bon voyage'. Little did they know about the German crew.

The *Portuguese Prince* sailed on to her port of destination without any further incident. La Plata is a port for the Argentine Navy, and many warships could be seen moored at the top end of the harbour, mostly old British ships. Some even had yards for sails, besides the steam power. There was very little wharfage for merchant ships, and the *Portuguese Prince* was apparently moored at the site on which the abattoir was to be built – a very temporary wooden wharf. As the steelwork of girders and other constructional work was being discharged, men were erecting it on the site.

The Captain apparently got his orders to discharge all German personnel at once, so this was done, and they were all immediately employed by the construction gang, slinging and securing the framework of the factory. Tom could see them every day from the ship, and often they came on board for a meal. No one had any grievance against those men, although they were now enemy personnel.

A new set of men came from Buenos Aires. They were either deserters from other British ships or from hospital, but they met their match with the Chief Officer and Second Engineer, whose business it was to control them. One bright young man, though, showed great promise, and Tom Sloane liked him very much. The German Bosun was allowed to carry on with the ship, as he was born in Heligoland when that North Sea island was under the British flag.

Eventually all the cargo was discharged, beside the steelwork, bricks and mortar and all building materials, and the ship proceeded to Buenos Aires to load a full cargo of grain for Santos. A new parson, Canon Brady, had control of the Seamen's Mission. He was another fine big man, and was soon well liked by all, typical of all Seamen's Mission parsons, although he had many other duties besides looking after seamen. He always visited each ship in the port every day, had the boxing ring in full operation and also personally took care of wayward seamen in that city of unlimited allurements.

Soon the ship was on its way to Santos, arriving there in due course, and after discharging the grain loaded the usual cargo for New Orleans and New York.

At Santos the apprentices did gangway duty, which meant that one boy did a period each day at the gangway in uniform. His duties were to keep undesirables off the ship, and take agents to the Captain or Chief Officer.

One day when Tom was doing his turn, one of the Negro stewards, a tall youth of nineteen, called Tom a dirty word, and Tom, although only aged fifteen, challenged him to a fight when he was off duty that night, and the word got around. Of course, Tom felt a little scared to meet this Negro, as he had neither the physique nor the height of his opponent, but he stuck to his guns as he had been insulted.

At 6 p.m. he came off duty and changed into his working togs, then came on deck. The others had seen to forming a ring and quite a big crowd had gathered. This was the first altercation he had been in, so come what may he was going to have a go, and when they squared up to each other, he just went into that steward blindly, with his fists going like fury. He lost all fear and fought like mad, and his opponent just dropped and then got up and ran. Tom had no thoughts in his head, nor could he remember much of what he was doing, and he was more surprised than anybody when he saw his adversary running away.

Tom had won an honourable fight, and preserved his honour, and the Negro youth came forward next morning and apologised.

There was plenty of work for the apprentices when loading bags of coffee. It was such a delicate cargo, and the holds had to be perfectly clean while the ship's side and bulkheads were draped with gunny cloths which also had to be clean.

The bags were carried up from the shore on the heads of men, some carrying three bags at a time, each bag weighing about seventy pounds. They were then thrown on a slide and so slid down to where the men were working at the stowage.

When the cargo to be taken was loaded the ship proceeded to the usual ports, then to Trinidad for bunker coal. There a police boat came off to the ship and took away the German Bosun for internment. He was a good man, and the crew all wished him well, hoping the war would soon be over.

On arriving at New Orleans Tom found that the ship was to go no further, but was to discharge all the cargo there and then fit out for carrying horses to France. At least this was a change for them. The young man who had been shipped at La Plata was promoted to Bosun, and a good one he proved to be.

After the cargo was out, the ship was taken to load the lower holds halfway up with coal. This was to act as ballast, then the coal was levelled off and floored off with wood, after which a host of carpenters swarmed all over the ship, building horse stalls on each deck. The ship had four decks, lower and upper 'tween decks, main deck and even the boat deck, to carry twelve hundred horses.

Then she sailed for Galveston to load the horses, arriving there at a new wooden wharf, as it was not built up as it is today. On shore, at this wharf, were these horses in corrals, supervised by several horsemen. The ship had taken about sixty men at the past port — ten foremen with one boss — to look after the horses in transit. They also carried a veterinary surgeon and a doctor for the crew, as the ship had over one hundred persons on board. The horses looked a sprightly lot, and Tom was informed that all were two-year-olds and from the Red River area.

It was certainly a sight seeing so many horses. There were typical men on horseback here who had the job to stop any panics and to get the horses on board.

The ship had side doors into the upper 'tween deck, steel doors on hinges. The ramps were set up to these doors. A passage to the doors was railed off; now the job was to get the animals aboard. They were very shy of going up the ramp. Eventually one of the riders brought up his horse, which seemed to be a quiet animal, and led the way; the others followed. The same was done on all four ramps. After that it was just a steady stream of horses gradually filling all the stalls; when each one was full a side board was slipped into place. There were also stalls on all the upper decks, even the wooden deck or promenade deck the passengers used to use. This went on until the ship was completely loaded.

Horses were everywhere — what a change from general cargoes! Fresh water was carried in the double bottom tanks and deep tanks, about three thousand gallons, which was piped to the various compartments. Hay, oats and bran were distributed in various other compartments to be handy to each hold.

The ship soon sailed from Galveston and her destination was La Pallice, the port for La Rochelle, halfway down the French west coast, bordering the Bay of Biscay.

The holds were kept open, with eight canvas windsails at each hold. The windsails were strung up on triatic stays to catch any breeze to get fresh air down to the lower tier of horses.

Tom was now on watches with the crew, four hours on and four hours off, but his duties were not arduous, as he was at the call of the officer on watch. The only job for the spare man of the watch was to trim the windsails, so that all the wind possible went down the hold.

Tom found the most comfortable place as the nights grew colder was on the steampipe casing around the Fidley, so he was handy for the bridge, and there he would sit warming his breeches. The night watchmen looking after the horses – about a round dozen of them – thought the same as Tom, and arranged themselves on the steampipe casing, too, when not doing their rounds.

These men were all hoboes. Tom had heard of such characters roaming all over the United States, and never costing themselves a cent. The United States was a great open country in those days before the 1914 war, and it was not so long since the Gold Rush days of 1898, when masses of human beings from Europe came over on anything that could sail the ocean. There were no immigration laws to stop them, and in all probability the hoboes were a throw off from those days. Some of these men had been well educated, while some had had family troubles and just hit the wide open spaces, finding other characters of the same nature. They were men of honour, and in no way brutal or bloodthirsty, and the yarns spun by these men in the dark hours of the night had Tom enthralled. Most of them were of British stock, and they travelled the country from coast to coast in the freight trains, or, as they called it, 'jumped the freight'.

When they wanted to move on any distance they just went down to the railway yard where some empty freight cars were making up and jumped in an empty car before the train left, and off they went to wherever the train was going.

The cars, which were covered-in railway wagons, offered quite good accommodation for these gentry, as they would either beg or steal food for the journey. The car would have plenty of straw or something to that effect from its last contents, to keep them warm,

As trains travelled great journeys they could be three or four days on them, or they could jump out at some stopping place and just lie about if the weather was suitable In the winter they knew of small towns where they could have the Sheriff lock them up in a nice warm jail and be fed for doing some work in return, but in the warm weather work was not for them.

Food was very cheap. If a man had five cents he could go into a bar, order a schooner of beer, and with it have a substantial free lunch of ham or beef sandwiches. Tom knew that this was possible as when in New York last he had found it an easy job to go into a bar, particularly one just outside the dock, which they did often in the evenings when staying on board, order a schooner of beer and give it to the person standing nearest to him. At the far end of the counter was a man in a white coat presiding over a large cold joint of beef and a ham, with the necessary large loaf of bread to make sandwiches. He would shout, 'What is it tonight, boys?', and soon four hefty sandwiches were made, which were taken back to the ship where they went down well with a pot of cocoa.

It may have been a flush of patriotism that induced these hoboes to sign on a horse transport, as this ship was. Maybe it was just love of horses, as most of them had worked as cowboys at some time in the past. They certainly knew all about horses, and could go into the stall of an excited horse or a sick one and soon calm down the first and administer to the other.

Their pay was a mere pittance, fifteen dollars out and twenty back for cleaning out and whitewashing the stalls. It is remarkable that not a horse died on that voyage, after fourteen days of standing. When a horse wanted to lie down it was sick, and should it lie down it would probably be kicked and trampled on by the horses on each side of it. When a horse was really sick it was brought up to one of the deck stalls, which acted as a sick bay. Sometimes many horses had to be moved to get the sick horse out, and this required tact and know-how, otherwise there would have been panic and confusion, which would have caused injuries to other horses.

After the first voyage to France and back to Galveston, our hobo friends were paid off, having done a good job.

The sailors and apprentices on the voyage back were employed night and day taking the coal out of No. 2 hold, which was there for ballast, and transferring this to the bunkers, as no coal was left in the bunkers on account of the horse stalls having been built there as in the other holds.

When all the horses were landed in La Pallice, fit and well, the French Army took them over, and it was another amazing sight to see truck-load after truck-load going off to the interior. True, the horses were lively when they landed, and some went off at a gallop with the lead man trailing behind. Only horsemen could handle them, and that was what the hoboes did.

The ship had to leave immediately the horses were out for quarantine reasons: while she stopped in port she stank to high heaven. When under way at sea the air was able to get through the ship and sweeten her. On the way back across the Atlantic the cattlemen had to clean the ship out and whitewash the stalls for the next load. They arrived at Galveston during February 1915. Tom cannot even remember where they spent Christmas Day. The ship lay in the stream for some time, at anchor, and the Chief Officer decided to have the overside painted grey, the usual colour, and as much of the boot-topping as possible. This is where Tom nearly lost his life.

He was in the punt around by the propeller, with the Bosun, to paint in the draft figures. The tide was running so strongly that it was splashing up against the propeller and filled the punt with water. Bailing was out of the question, as it was filling all the time, and would soon be dragged under. The after rope was let go and the punt swung out, then capsized, throwing Tom out, with the Bosun hanging on to the forward painter.

As Tom swept past the ship with a pair of rubber boots on, which were rapidly filling up with water, his thought was that he did not want to lose those boots as he had just swopped a pair of leather sea boots for them that day. The leather ones had hurt his feet.

Fortunately, a fireman saw Tom being carried away from the ship. Leaning over the rail just above, he flung a lifebuoy with a small line attached right ahead of Tom who soon grabbed hold of it, and as soon as the rope took the strain he swung around with the force of the tide, and away went his boots. The fireman got assistance to haul on the line, but only slowly, as the line might have parted. He was hauled along to a rope ladder over the side and eventually climbed up on to the deck. If that fireman had not been there Lord knows what would have happened to Tom.

The ship arrived at New Orleans again and berthed at a wharf alongside the railway. They had in addition to their cattlemen, an Italian veterinary surgeon and about five assistants, all army people. This time fifty Negroes were taken on as cattlemen, with the same foremen as before. The horses came in by train alongside the ship, and as soon as the train arrived the horses were run on board. Some even dropped dead as soon as they stepped out of the train. About fifty horses died on that voyage. They would die in some out of the way corner of the hold, probably through lack of good air.

Anyhow the ship got her load and was bound for Genoa in Italy this time. It was the Bosun's and the sailors' job to get the dead horses out of the hold on to the top of the stalls on deck. Of course, the apprentices on watch were in the gang. It was quite a feat to get a dead horse out. A series of snatch blocks were secured at strategic points along the gangways between the horse stalls, and after the dead horse was removed from his stall a rope strop was secured around the neck and a wire runner passed through all the snatch blocks and hooked on to the strop; generally the horse was well distended with internal gases. When all was set the wire runner which was on the winch was hove away, dragging the body along clear ways; as each snatch block was reached the wire was taken out, following the various tracks the body had to go before reaching a clear lift out of the hold. It was then landed on top of the deck stalls and pushed overboard. When the ship was rolling they had to watch they did not go over with the dead horse. Some days they were doing nothing else but dump the dead ones, especially as the weather became warmer. The windsails needed constant trimming to the wind — this was not an easy job especially in the dark as the guys would soon mix up into a rare tangle, but it was all necessary to get fresh air down into the holds.

A considerable number of people came down to watch the horses being landed. The Italian Army took the horses away, and again, for quarantine reasons, the ship had to sail immediately, this time for New York. The same procedure was gone through as on the last voyage.

On arriving at New York the ship went to Yonkers for the next load. On both sides of the East River were green fields as far as one could see. The horses were on the New Jersey side, and came off to the ship in barges to be loaded for Brest in France. The ship came back to New York again after delivering the horses at Brest, a quick turn-round.

During the last voyage Tom had on that ship from New York to Brest, he developed the symptoms of appendicitis, or so the ship's doctor diagnosed. He had to lie up, and on arrival at Brest the shore doctor came aboard and told the Captain it would be better to take Tom to hospital.

He was berthed in a bed with quite a number of miscellaneous individuals in the other beds. The doctor looked him over and left him there for a day or two, after which he was wheeled off into the operating room. It was a Roman Catholic hospital, and the nurses wore nuns' garments.

Tom watched the doctor sharpening up his instruments on a razor strop, and promptly informed him that he would not have the operation done, so he was wheeled out again and put to bed. The agents were informed and also the British Consul who, like Pontius Pilate, said he washed his hands of Tom for refusing to be operated upon. Tom said he now felt no pain, and had not done for some considerable time, but the doctor had insisted he should be treated as an invalid.

The doctor allowed him to leave the hospital; in fact, he was discharged bag and baggage. He tottered down to the waterfront, and saw a ship alongside called the *George Fisher*. His legs were weak through being laid up so long, but eventually he got on board, wearing his apprentice's uniform, and asked the Captain to take him home to England. He had no money to pay for his passage, but when the Captain heard his tale he immediately gave his permission, and Tom was put under the Chief Steward's care.

The *George Fisher* was going to Swansea, and after Tom had had a good strong cup of tea and something to eat, the Second Mate took him over and showed him how to oil the steering gear.

The Captain saw to it that he had his meals with him, and said he would pay Tom's fare to his home, which he did going across to Swansea from Brest. Tom spent some time on the bridge steering the ship to allow the sailor to help in the work on deck.

Arriving in Swansea, Tom was amazed to see the runners from the ship chandlers pestering the Captain for his orders, as the Captain fed the ship and supplied the tobacco.

Anyhow Tom was put in charge of one of these runners and taken to the railway station and seen off to his home town. His parents did not know Tom was coming home, so he gave them a pleasant surprise when he knocked them up at six o'clock one morning.

Next day Tom reported to the company's office and the gentleman with the white whiskers, the Marine Superintendent, gazed on him as if he had been washed up with the tide. He did not know that he had been left in hospital and then discharged.

No doubt his first thoughts were that Tom had deserted his ship, and when the facts were straightened out it still did not look good, by the response he received. But Tom would not have wanted to desert – he was satisfied with the sea life. However, Tom returned home to await another ship.

It was about the end of September 1915, and having been out of the country since before the war he was quite taken aback at seeing most males in khaki or in Naval uniform. Soldiers were training in the nearby fields, digging trenches or bayoneting large stuffed bags hanging from tree branches.

Immense activity was going on everywhere. With soldiers marching to the trains on the way to France, there was not a dull moment. Tom was called up, although he was only sixteen years old, but after an interview he was told to go back to his ship.

Tom had about three weeks at home, and was then sent to Hull to join the *Ocean Prince*, only just arrived from the River Plate. This would be late in the year 1915. The apprentice he relieved had completed his indentures. The other three apprentices were all fine chaps, and very keen on studying for their 2nd Mate certificates. Tom had done a considerable amount of ground work in his studying in his watches below while on the last ship, on his own, with the other chaps' books. As Tom had not attended any secondary school he had to start from the bottom and learn the first principles of trigonometry, first plain and then spherical, which somehow he mastered, those subjects being the root of all navigation, as well as logarithms. On the *Ocean Prince* at least two of the apprentices were well advanced so Tom fell in very well with them. They worked all their navigation from Admiralty books, which could be obtained from home dockyards as they visited them quite a lot in the twelve months Tom served on this vessel.

Chapter 3

THE *Ocean Prince* was a regular tramp ship and what was termed a three-island ship, having a forecastle head, amidship house and a poop. Sailors and firemen lived under the forecastle head, deck officers lived on the starboard side and engineer officers on the portside, amidships. Cooks and stewards were housed close to the store-room or galley. When the ship was built no doubt the builders and the shipowner waited until the vessel was completed and if any space was available they knocked something up for those bright young lads, the four apprentices.

The accommodation for the apprentices on this ship must have been a converted store-room for the engineers, as it was just outside the engine room door, at the after end of the bridge deck. When the four bunks were in place it only left enough room for a table to seat two. Being close to the door the doorstep was convenient for the other two.

The SS *Ocean Prince* was about eight thousand tons deadweight, and for all her faults she was a happy ship. Captain and officers were very good men, and what is more they took an interest in the apprentices. The engineers were not far behind in being affable and friendly, and Tom felt more comfortable and easy on this ship than ever he did on the *Portuguese Prince*.

His fellow apprentices were fine chaps too. One was Max Henderson, who incidentally lived close to Tom's aunt and uncle in Newcastle and so had heard of Tom before, the other two chaps being Scott and Gregory. The latter's father was a hotelier on the Isle of Wight, while Max Henderson had been to Rutherford College before taking up the sea. His extra knowledge helped Tom a great deal with his studies.

Submarine war had not started so far, but raiders could be expected. When in the dockyards a naval signalman would take the officers and apprentices in visual signalling, and they soon became proficient in morse and semaphore. In fact, they would communicate with each other by semaphore as much as possible by spelling out the words with their arms. They also made a morse lamp out of a half pound tobacco tin by making a small hole in it; this hole they covered by a shutter worked with a piece of sail twine fixed with a small screw at the side so that it could go up and down. Inside the tin they had a lighted candle. They wasted no time in mastering that little device, and the morse code, at a reasonable speed.

SS *Ocean Prince.*

The ship was taken over by the Admiralty and given a number, A.C.193, and was employed running between Montreal or Halifax, Nova Scotia, to south coast dockyards or French Channel ports. Every voyage homewards the ship carried four fast motor boats for the Navy, which were taken off at Portsmouth. These were used for raiding and carried two torpedoes and a 12-pounder gun.

The North Atlantic was a hard trade, and when the outward passage was in ballast it was common to take twenty-one days in the crossing. The ship rolled like the very devil, and made little headway in the prevailing westerly gales. On one voyage a man was lost overboard through the ship rolling. Of course, homeward bound she ran with the wind and sea behind her, but sometimes that was not comfortable when the seas were very high in the gale force winds. The *Ocean Prince*'s best speed in a calm sea was nine knots.

The funnel was a worry. The ship bunkered at Cardiff, taking best Welsh coal. As the funnel had no outer casing it would become red-hot, and it was a wonder it did not set the ship on fire. The wire guys were only secured to the deck by rope lashings, and these had to be slacked off when the funnel was on fire. Eventually a large hole was burnt in the front. This was covered up by sheets of asbestos, and lashed in place by wire, and she carried those sheets of asbestos until the end of her days.

On one voyage outward they encountered bad weather all the way down the Channel and when she got out into the open Atlantic they were blown down into the Bay of Biscay and towards the French coast. An island appeared to leeward during the night, and as the ship was not handling well she came very close to being piled up on a lee shore. It was so alarming that the Captain sent Tom to call all hands who might be sleeping and get everyone to dress in warm clothes to be ready for any emergency if she could not clear. But by some miracle she just did so. If there had been any offshore rocks she would have had it. But getting around, the Captain made for a sheltered bay. Next thing to think about was to replenish the bunker coal, so he took her into Brest.

One hundred and fifty tons was granted by the French, which came off in lighters, to be loaded by the crew. Tom was in the barge, shovelling and filling baskets to be hauled up by the winch; hard work for a boy of seventeen. After three days the ship sailed again, into bad weather all the way, taking twenty-seven days from her port of departure to Sidney, Cape Breton.

Tom remembered the ship as a happy one for the crew, simply because they all had to pull their weight and there was no time for pettiness, as on a ship always trading in fine weather. Fine weather ships were always polishing up something, scrubbing decks, painting this and that from 6 a.m. to 6 p.m. until this became boring.

The old *Ocean Prince* seemed to be a ship where something was happening all the time, and if you got a fine day everybody doubly enjoyed it. On one voyage the engineers had about twenty barrels of engine oil lashed on deck. This broke away in the middle of one night, and a couple of sailors and Tom were sent to secure the rolling barrels. But some of them had been smashed and there was oil all over the decks. They could not keep their feet, and what with that and the ship rolling heavily it was a wonder they got any saved at all. It was like trying to secure a pack of mad dogs.

As mentioned before, the ship went to Halifax, but only in the winter when the St Lawrence was frozen up. It was cold there, so the Captain bought the apprentices a coal bogey and had its funnel sticking out of the after port. The bogey was grand for making tea and toast at any time, and the Second and Third Mates often came down for a cup of 'Rosy Lee'.

On this ship the apprentices were on regular watches with the sailors, keeping the usual hours at the wheel and look-out. As they approached home waters they had to take a watch with the officer, to help with signal flags and look out for enemy ships, so Tom felt he was just about covering all the duties of a seaman. In port they had afternoons off for studying. All were interested and helped each other, and Tom so liked studying that his text books were the only ones he read.

Halifax was a Naval port, also a port for collecting troops for transport to the UK. One evening when ashore Tom saw a most amusing incident when the troops arranged a recruiting march through the main street. The Canadian Scottish were to the fore with their drums and pipes leading the march, and down the sides of the street were soldiers raking in all the males. They would not take 'no' for an answer, and when they met any Navy men they were roped in, too. As the soldiers were in large numbers they soon quelled any resistance.

The next night in Barrington Street, the main thoroughfare with the Navy yard down at the far end, the Navy lads marched down, but they only had a band of four banjos in front. They marched in the usual soft shoe manner to the twanging of the banjos while recruiting men walked down the side of the pavement on each side, and it was most amusing to watch them rope in the soldiers to join the Navy. Tom thought it was a pleasant rivalry between the soldiers and the Naval men, and that the Navy must have picked their fattest and biggest men.

It was from this port that General Wolfe mustered all his ships and men for the assault on Quebec in the 1760s and no doubt Captain Cook in his early days surveyed the St Lawrence river and the coast of Newfoundland, which through time made possible the hoisting of the British flag over Canada.

But it was now 1916 and Halifax was a port for the departure of Canadian troops and ships, going the opposite way to General Wolfe, to help in overthrowing Britain's enemies.

On one voyage Tom's ship came to London – the only time she did go there, having a load of bulk grain from Montreal. It was in November 1916, and the ship was moored in South West India Dock, about two hundred yards from the quayside, to buoys ahead and astern. This dock was usually used for timber, and great stacks of it were on the shore all round the dock. The *Ocean Prince* went there so that she could discharge over both sides into lighters.

The weather was miserable, always raining. The ship was discharged, the crew was paid off and a new crew was waiting to be signed on. The ship had just completed discharging at No. 4 hold, abaft the amidship deck.

Only the officers and apprentices were on board, and at midnight, all being asleep in their bunks (a shore watchman being employed), the Captain woke them with the news that No. 4 hold was on fire, and smoke was coming out of the ventilators.

Tom and his shipmates got a hose out, but on opening the hatchway to see where the fire was, the smoke came out so thickly that they could see nothing at all. So the hatch was closed again and the covers put on the ventilators to stop the air blowing down into the hold.

Tom was dispatched to take the small sculler boat to the shore and inform the police at the dock gate of the fire and call the fire brigade. Off he went with just a jersey and pants on in the pouring rain, and arriving at the dockside he had to run about half a mile to the gate. The policeman on duty was sitting in his box, which was no bigger than a sentry box, and he was fast asleep. When Tom yelled at him that the *Ocean Prince* was on fire and required the fire brigade the policeman jumped up with a start, and in so doing struck the top of his box with his helmet, thereby jamming the helmet hard on his head. He was properly awake then. He dashed into his office and with the aid of an antiquated telephone got in touch with the fire department. Tom had to wait for them, to show the way to the ship, and after about an hour's wait they arrived – four men with a hand cart, with hoses on the cart. Tom urged them to hurry, so they all trotted down to the dockside where the boat was, threw the hoses in the boat and then themselves, nearly sinking it.

The rain was coming down in a steady downpour as Tom sculled the boat off to the ship. Up the accommodation ladder they went with the hoses, finding when they tried to connect to the ship's service that the hoses would not fit. They had a look down the hatch, then all trundled back to the boat again.

Tom put them ashore to get extra equipment, and they soon turned up again with more men and smoke helmets. Tom sculled them back to the ship in relays, then had to take the connecting ends of the hoses to the shore where they were connected to hydrants – a very long length of hose, which took time to connect up. By then Tom could not have been more wet if he had fallen overboard.

No sooner were some of the firemen put on board than others wanted to go ashore. They all looked the same to Tom after about a couple of hours. When the fire was out they all decided to go ashore with their gear. He could see that they had had something to keep the damp out, so Tom went into the galley and over a hot cup of coffee got his clothes dried and his body warm again. Daylight was gradually showing on that cold wet morning in November. The hoses had to be disconnected and taken ashore, together with all the firemen.

The other apprentices, too, had had their work cut out and were all glad to see the last of the fire. The hold being now open looked as black as could be and a most depressing place. Much damage was done, the wooden ceiling over the tank tops and all the spar ceiling on the ship's side being burnt to cinders, while several frames and beams were distorted. The wooden hatches had also been badly burnt and rendered useless.

The company's Superintendent with Lloyd's surveyors were aboard in the forenoon to ascertain the damage in order to arrange for repairs. Ship repair men got going, and in three days the ship was ready for sea

A painting of SS *Ocean Prince* by Bruce Clark.

again. Soon the crew were signed on and the ship was away on her voyage to Canada.

The old *Ocean Prince* was not lacking in incidents, and Tom recalls being bound from Montreal to Devonport with a full load of ammunition. Two days before arrival at her destination a destroyer escort met the ship to escort her into port.

The apprentices took a bridge watch with the officer to take signals. The warship commenced signalling next day by hand flags giving an account of a battle going on in the North Sea between the British and German big ships. The messages seemed to cover all British ships that were being sunk one after another, and the news was very bad indeed. In due course the *Ocean Prince* docked at Devonport, then received the news that the German ships had fled back to Germany, being just as seriously damaged as the British ships. That was the Battle of Jutland.

The *Ocean Prince* was berthed on the riverside under the big crane, when she had to go off into the stream again to make way for the battleship *Barham* which had been very badly damaged. Coming in at the berth just vacated by the *Ocean Prince*, she was a mess, having come from the Battle of Jutland. There were great gaping holes in her and twisted steel deck structure, together with a heavy list, and the dockyard maties had a gruesome job recovering the bodies of her crew who had been trapped in the wreckage. It was a sad sight.

After Tom's ship had discharged her cargo safe and sound, she proceeded to Falmouth to take on ballast for the first time. The deep tanks being of no use for holding water, about two hundred tons of slag ballast was dropped into them, this coming up to the height of the tunnel for the propeller shaft, about eight feet. In addition one hundred tons of sand ballast was taken in the 'tween deck above the deep tank. Wooden hatches were fitted over the deep tank instead of steel lids, and when the ship was out at sea the crew had to trim the sand ballast, up against each side of the engine room bulkhead, and then board it so that it would remain there.

It was six o'clock one wild morning, and the crew had started work on this trimming. Tom was on watch when the Chief Officer sent him down the hatch to find the Bosun for something or other.

When Tom climbed down the hold it was very dark, but he could see the flickering candles where the men were working. He did not know that several hatches were off the deep tank, and as he made to walk across to them he disappeared down the deep tank, falling about twelve feet and landing on the lumpy slag. The men saw him go and the carpenter brought Tom up on his back. The pain in his back was very severe and he lost consciousness. He was placed in the spare room off the saloon, but there was not much anyone could do for him so Tom had to sweat it out on his own. He lay for four weeks, two weeks of that in Halifax harbour, in sheer misery.

To take his mind off it, he forced himself to study his seamanship book and in due course he memorised all the 'Rule of the Road' articles, which is quite a feat as they covered the rules and regulations of every type of craft afloat.

Tom gradually recovered as the pain got less. He took exercise each day until he was strong enough to take his place again with his fellow apprentices.

The *Ocean Prince* discharged motor launches at Portsmouth several times. It was usual to anchor off Gosport for a few days until the big crane was ready for them, and during that time the Captain would go ashore each day, so the apprentices had a good job keeping the boat clean and sailing her ashore with the old man at the tiller, or if the wind was no good the four of them manned the oars. It was good practice.

The old man would stop ashore all day, so the boys had to wait for him. They wore jerseys and blue trousers along with a uniform cap with badge. The dress was neat enough, so off they would go and talk to the nursemaids on the promenade. Gregory seemed to be the expert at contacting the girls. Tom always felt such an oaf at this job, but the girls sometimes took a fancy to him because of his shyness. Nevertheless he could never get down to their line of chat. But it all helped to pass the time away, as one never knew when the old man was coming back. It was generally about nine o'clock at night, and they had to have a few sandwiches, prepared by the steward, to help them out.

The first time the ship went into this port she lay alongside a wooden jetty, while on the other side lay the old wooden warship, HMS *Excellent*, a training ship for seamen. Tom and his pals would lean over the rail and watch men drilling on deck. It was about noon one day, when the sailors were dismissed from drilling, that one of them darted over to the *Ocean Prince*. He came right down to the apprentices' room and the other chaps immediately recognised him as the chap who had left them in Hull to go up for his Second Mate's ticket when Tom joined the ship.

He was in tears as he told his story. Apparently when he entered the School of Navigation at Liverpool he was persuaded to join Lord Derby's scheme, as then he would not be conscripted. The scheme provided an armlet, blue with a crown worked on it, which was worn on the right arm, and he was told he would be as safe as houses under this scheme. But he had only been at the school a month when the whole school sitting for Second Mate's tickets were ordered to report to headquarters for service in the Navy. So that was where he ended up, with no certificate at all.

They heard later that he was allowed time to sit for his certificate, which he eventually got, but he was still in the Navy and was promoted to sub-lieutenant. Such was life in war-time – as bad as the press gang.

On one voyage they left Halifax looking very peaceful, well wooded and as it has always looked since the British were stationed there. A fortnight after they left there was a big explosion, and when they returned the whole scene had altered – not a tree was standing; it was as bald as a coot, and the whole of Richmond, on the inland side of the town, had been blown to bits. What a mess! Hundreds of men, women and children had been killed. The whole city was in mourning.

During the summer months the *Ocean Prince* sailed up the St Lawrence to Montreal where she loaded her cargo for the UK. A bridge was being built across the St Lawrence at Quebec. The two arms of the bridge were completed and the centre section, weighing five thousand tons, was to be lifted to complete the job. The ship passed up the river the night before this operation was to be carried out.

The centre mass of steelwork was lying on floats ready to be put in place next morning. On arriving at Montreal next day, news came through that the jacks had failed and the whole of the centre section had fallen and sunk to the river bottom, taking with it twenty-five men who were on the lifting operation of this structure.

The old *Ocean Prince* was a bad ship for rats, which would nest everywhere, even in the coils of the mooring ropes forward and aft. Every time the ropes were moved they would jump out as though from a conjurer's hat, and down the holds they were countless.

On her last voyage in the middle of December 1916 she was bound for Cherbourg in North-West France, for orders from Halifax, with a full load of oats, after a reasonably good voyage across. The ship was approaching the north-west coast, the night being dark and the sky heavy with clouds. No lights or aids to navigation were exhibited, and the ship was blacked out too.

Two faint white lights were seen on the starboard bow, and were mistaken for a ship's dimmed steaming lights, so Tom was instructed to plug in the mainmast navigation light. The plug and socket were just under the crosstree, and Tom did what he was told, which meant going up the rigging. He had landed again on deck when with a series of bumps the ship ran over the rocks.

She stuck fast, and in no time number one hold was filling up with water. The bottom had been torn open. The Chief Officer called Tom and the carpenter to come along with him forward to sound around. The rats were coming out in hundreds from the fore peak and jumping over the side, and the sailors and firemen had to shut the doors to keep them out of their forecastle.

In time the lifeboat came off, but they did not leave the ship, as she seemed safe enough. The lifeboat went back to shore and put the lighthouse light on. It was so near that it nearly blinded them all, for the ship was actually ashore at the foot of Cape la Hague lighthouse, and the lights they had seen from the bridge were from a house on shore.

One bulkhead after another burst with a bang until the ship's engine room was flooded. The fires in the boiler room had been drawn in time. The old funnel collapsed at last — a sad ending to an old ship. Although she had had her troubles, she had never let them down, Tom reflected. She even put them on the rocks instead of in the deep sea on a reasonably fine night.

The next morning two salvage tugs closed in on the ship. Getting as near as was possible, they put suction pipes on board in the engine room to try to pump out the water. Much water passed through the pumps and the level of the water was going down, but it was found that it was because the tide was doing the same.

The ship's lifeboats had been put into the water, and Tom was sent into one to look after the boats. It was decided to abandon the old *Ocean Prince*, so the crew were taken off on to the salvage tug. The ship's two lifeboats were taken away too, being towed astern of the tug, with Tom in command of them.

When their ship went ashore in the end she was a total loss. She was a bad ship for rats, but when she started to break up it seemed that there were thousands of them coming out of the holds and swarming all over the decks. No doubt they swam ashore, as they do on all shipwrecks.

The crew were landed at Cherbourg, which was twelve miles to the eastward of the wreck, the port she had originally been bound for. They were housed in the French Naval barracks for two days until a cross-Channel ship arrived, which took them all to Southampton, where they were dispatched to their home ports.

Apprentice Scott had completed his indentures, having been acting as Bosun for some time, and had now to present himself to the Board of Trade for the examination for Second Mate. He went off home, and as Gregory's home was on the Isle of Wight, he departed too. Tom never saw either of them again, although he heard later on in life that Scott, who gained his certificates, was lost in one of the China coast ships which disappeared in a typhoon.

Only Max Henderson and Tom were able to present themselves to the company's office at Newcastle, and they arrived at their homes on 24 December 1916. Tom had completed three years' service and Max Henderson three and a half years, so they both felt that the worst was over regarding their apprenticeship. The war being in full swing, however, it was not wise to look too far ahead.

Tom spent the Christmas and New Year at home, but, strange to say, he was too restless to appreciate being in the midst of the family circle again, much as he tried to. The rough and tumble of life on board ship had got into his bones, and the companionship of his fellow shipmates was missed. He could not find that companionship ashore.

Chapter 4

EARLY IN THE NEW YEAR OF 1917, Tom was instructed to join the SS *Asiatic Prince* at Sunderland – a ship of about 4,500 tons deadweight. He had not told his parents he was short of clothing, as most had been left in the wreck of the *Ocean Prince*. Instead, off he went with his little bundle by train to Sunderland.

Stepping out of the train on arrival at his destination was another apprentice of his own age, also bound for the *Asiatic Prince*. Names were exchanged, his new-found shipmate being Frank Thornton. On boarding the ship Tom found Max Henderson there, together with three other apprentices. It was understood that two would be transferring to another ship on reaching Buenos Aires, the two being Tom and the youngest boy, Ted Davis, who had nine months' time in. Tom had only eleven months to go to complete his indentures. The other two boys were Jack Smith and Peter Thompson, who both had about a year to do. Jack Smith was an ex-choirboy of Durham Cathedral.

The ship was loading creosoted wooden sleepers for the Argentine railways, and when this was completed and the crew had signed on, she left for London to load and complete everything there. Tom was on watch with the seamen taking wheel and look-out. He felt the cold winds badly on the ship's open bridge, with no shelter at all standing at the steering wheel. Mines were the hazard in the North Sea; and two ships were blown up this way. The Captain sent their lifeboat to pick up survivors, and the crews were rescued and taken on to London. Frank Thornton was in the lifeboat as soon as it was lowered, as he was not on watches.

The *Asiatic Prince* docked at Royal Albert Dock and loaded a cargo of a very valuable nature for Buenos Aires. It was said that this cargo would pay for another cargo home.

When loaded the ship proceeded on her way south to Buenos Aires. No doubt submarines were about, but none interfered with the ship's progress down-Channel.

Out in the open sea going south, raiders could be met at any time, so the Captain had the forecastle bell rigged up on top of the engine room, with a line attached to the bridge. This was rung when any ship was sighted to warn the engineers to give all speed to keep out of sight, and the Captain would turn the ship away for that purpose.

At this time merchant ships were beginning to be fitted with a gun on the stern for protection. The *Asiatic Prince* had a twelve-pounder on the stern with two Naval ratings to keep it in order, and the apprentices were trained by them as gun's crew. It was the practice to turn the ship stern on to any ship sighted so that she could be in a position to fire this gun if the ship should be proved to be hostile. They also had a very large red ensign, about three yards square, which should be hoisted at the mast top if the gun had to be used.

One day, about one week out, a ship was sighted. Although the Captain was steering away from it and keeping it astern, the stranger was quickly overhauling them and turned out to be a warship. The gun was manned and ammunition was ready, but he signalled by flags that he was a British ship, asking where the *Asiatic Prince* was bound and if she had sighted anything suspicious. A couple of the lads went up on the bridge to handle the flags of the international code. After the warship was satisfied he turned about and disappeared over the horizon. Such an incident made everyone think that some enemy ship must be about. However, no other incident happened on the voyage south.

As the weather became warmer Tom and his messmates began enjoying their dog watches by learning to sing under the direction of Jack Smith, the ex-choirboy. Soon they mastered, in their own way, a few songs, sung in parts without any accompanying music. Frank Thornton was literally quite a big noise in singing, so they passed away the dog watches very pleasantly, keeping their minds off any calamities that might happen if an enemy raider did come on the scene.

In course of time the *Asiatic Prince* arrived at Buenos Aires and docked in South Dock, a rather dubious part of the city, so they soon had Canon Brady on board, inviting them all up to the Seamen's Mission. There, of course, they met other apprentices off ships in the port.

It soon got around that the *Asiatic Prince* apprentices could sing. It must have been Frank Thornton who spread this news as he was very anxious to have them all up on the stage to do their bit. So they organised themselves and did one or two concerts, which seemed to go down well.

The ship that was to take two of the apprentices finally arrived in port, and Tom was surprised to hear that he did not have to go after all, Frank Thornton being sent over with Ted Davis. Frank did not like the move at all, but he had to do as he was told.

The general opinion on the half deck was that the Chief Officer, Mr James, had persuaded the Captain to make this alteration. It was hinted that Frank Thornton's home in South Shields was close to the Chief

Officer's home and he knew the family well. The Chief Officer's parents and sisters were strict Salvation Army people, but he himself was a bit of a lad and liked to see the bright lights, together with its pleasures. So it would suit the Chief Officer well to have Frank out of his orbit, as he would not care for such a publicity agent.

Well, so be it; Frank and Ted had to go and the rest were sorry to see them leave. The move suited Tom as he was happy on this ship, and anyhow, Frank's indentures would be completed in six months' time.

The ship was soon unloaded and sailing for Bahia Blanca, which was out of the River Plate, about a day's run down the coast. There she was to load a full cargo of tinned corned beef and tongues for a French port, where it would go to the Army.

On arriving at Bahia Blanca, they found two large British sailing ships there, the *Falkirk* and the *Port Jackson*, both full-rigged ships. The first had six apprentices and the other about twenty cadets, as she was a school ship belonging to Davit and Moore of Southampton. The *Falkirk* was registered at Leith. In Bahia Blanca there was a small Seamen's Mission run by a middle-aged padre who had his wife and daughter with him.

The padre soon introduced Tom and his messmates to the sailing ship's crowd, and found them all exceedingly nice chaps. They visited each other's ships, and they were allowed to run up the rigging to see what it was like aloft.

On the *Falkirk* the old Second Mate – or at least he seemed old to Tom – even had them doing stunts by racing up the mizzen mast, over the truck and down the other side, which they did in creditable time for steamship boys.

They played each other at football on many occasions and had concerts at the Mission. No other ships were in port at that time. The padre's daughter was about seventeen, a charming girl indeed, and she kept all the boys in order. The padre mentioned that he had accepted an offer to go to Tristan da Cunha, to take over the church there, where he went shortly after the ships left.

The *Falkirk* sailed first, and it was quite a sight seeing her going under tow, with all the crew up in the rigging cheering like mad. The *Port Jackson*'s crew were doing likewise, and so were the crew of the *Asiatic Prince*. It was the usual practice when sailing ships left port to have such a send-off. The *Falkirk* was going around the Horn to Australia. The same ceremony was carried out when the *Port Jackson* left, but when the *Asiatic Prince* was loaded there was no one to cheer her out except the padre and his family.

It was Captain Brown's practice to have an apprentice to steer the ship out of port under the pilot's or his directions, so Tom was at the wheel on the way out of Bahia Blanca, *en route* for Cherbourg for orders.

Although the ship had wireless this was only for receiving purposes. The general messages sent out from the Admiralty were the positions of enemy craft which had been sighted.

The voyage homewards was uneventful. Gun drill was practised about once a week, when a target would be dropped overboard and the Captain would have the ship brought round at intervals so that the firing could be done at different angles. The two Naval ratings would handle the firing and the laying of the gun, while the apprentices loaded it. The magazines to hold the spare ammunition were on the gun plat-form. The gun was only meant to keep off a submarine or other craft within reason while wireless messages were sent out for aid. Many Allied warships were on patrol on the shipping routes, as Germany had put submarine operations into being, to sink all Allied ships on sight, without mercy.

All the ammunition had had to be landed in the care of the authorities at Buenos Aires and Bahia Blanca as the Argentine was a neutral country. It was placed in a barge outside the port and re-loaded when leaving.

Approaching Cherbourg, the *Asiatic Prince* passed fairly close to Cape la Hague lighthouse, and in daylight the wreck of the *Ocean Prince* could be seen quite plainly, with the funnel lying over at an unusual angle. That was the last time she was sighted.

At Cherbourg the Captain had to go on shore each day to await orders. The jolly-boat was used, so he would sail ashore with a couple of the apprentices as crew. On arriving, other ships' boats were there too, at the steps on the quay. The boat had to stay there until the Captain came off to the ship again.

Eventually he came with orders to discharge at Calais, so there the ship went, to be discharged by a labour force of Mongolians attached to the British Army. They wore the hat of the Royal Marines, and an officer and a sergeant attached to the Marines were in charge of each gang. In all probability the officer and sergeant were in the shipping business in peacetime. They were named 'Aly Sloper's Army' – trust the Army to find a nickname.

After discharging at Calais orders were received to proceed to London, and the ship sailed, without escort, arriving in the month of May 1917. The crew were paid off, and most rejoined after a few days off. The ship was once again in the Royal Albert Dock.

Now she was to load for Archangel in the White Sea. This was a war cargo, so it was all very exciting for the apprentices. To finish off the loading, several buoys were shipped in the holds and on deck. These were for laying in the White Sea for a swept channel, as the ice was only just breaking up in that area. Trucks were loaded on deck, and Tom noticed on a nameplate, at the side of the driver's cabin, the instructions that twelve miles per hour was the limit.

In addition to the vessel's crew and two gunners, two officers and eight men from Trinity House were taking passage for the purpose of laying the buoys. The *Asiatic Prince* had accommodation for twelve passengers, so the ship had the room for these men.

All hands were supplied with a heavy duffle coat with hood and trousers of the same material along with gloves, as the ship would be going into the Arctic Ocean.

They proceeded to Lerwick in the Shetlands, steaming along in the swept channel all the way up the coast. From Lerwick she steamed to Bergen where two pilots were shipped to take the ship inside the fjords to the North Cape. Being early June it would be constant daylight when rounding the Cape in the Land of the Midnight Sun, and this part of the voyage was most interesting for all on board. Tom, steering the ship to pilot's directions, found the scenery awesome and, of course, the magnetic compasses were of little use owing to the magnetic disturbance caused by the high mountains on each side of the channel, there being much iron ore in those mountains.

Attractive townships could be seen at the water's edge wherever there was room for them, and houses could be seen, too, on slopes high up in the mountains, which must have been most inconvenient to get to and away from, or so it seemed from a passing ship. Nevertheless it all looked very green and beautiful, although there was much snow on the top of the high land.

The ship stopped at one of these towns, and two other pilots took over, the pilots from Bergen going off. In time, when reaching clear water, all pilots left, and the ship steamed as far as seventy-five degrees north. Warm clothing was a blessing in those waters for Tom and his shipmates, as the wind from the north was biting.

Eventually they made the first port of call – Romanoff, later called Ukanski. Three British warships were lying in this inlet and had been all the winter, having been frozen in. Now the ice had just cleared, releasing a plague of mosquitoes, the biggest Tom had ever seen, and their bite was terrific.

The *Asiatic Prince* had stores and mail for these warships. They were *Hyphegenia*, *Intrepid* and *Vindictive* – all cruisers and all to make their name in the Zeebrugge affair later in the year. The stores were discharged into the *Intrepid*, and officers and seamen from these ships came on board and assisted the crew to discharge their stores. They must have been pleased to receive them after being frozen in and in perpetual darkness during the winter months.

From there the ship sailed for the White Sea and Archangel. Instructions had been received from the warship that the buoys were not to be laid, as the Russian revolution was developing rapidly and Russia had already come to terms with Germany. They were to be taken back to England in due course.

Arriving off Archangel there were three or four other ships at anchor, so the *Asiatic Prince* anchored and remained so for about three days.

They eventually steamed up a small river to the town, passing a wharf with eight ships alongside which were complete wrecks. The previous year the whole place had blown up. The ships and the wharf had been loaded with ammunition, much life being lost.

Close by at another wooden wharf the ship tied up and commenced discharging by local labour. The Russians seemed to be decent enough chaps, but very dispirited, which was no wonder with their country in the throes of a bloody revolution. Archangel appeared to be the last Royalist port, and if they could be given any clothing the Russians were very pleased, as they seemed destitute.

After the cargo was out, the ship went higher up the river and loaded a full cargo of baled hemp. That was a desolate place, but nevertheless, the weather being warm, the people were cheerful. Men and women bathed in the waters with not a stitch of clothing on, which seemed to be the thing to do.

When loaded, all the mail from troops all over Russia was taken on board, and she sailed back the way she had come. The whole voyage took only five weeks. It was not uncommon to pass German ships in the fjords, as these were neutral waters, and sometimes the crews would cheer each other.

The *Asiatic Prince* loaded again for Archangel from London, and so proceeded back there, but this time the darkness was setting in. She did not receive much cargo homewards, but she took about fifty refugees back to England.

A third voyage was made to Archangel with food and clothing, and now the weather was taking on a winter look, snow was coming down heavily and it was exceedingly cold. Tom knew she would not make another voyage there as the 'freeze-up' would surely make the waters unmanageable. His apprenticeship was nearing completion.

All the strays and refugees were taken on board. There must have been about fifty of them, governesses, teachers, British and French people who had been employed in the homes of the aristocrats. The Bolsheviks had come to some agreement with Germany, and as far as they were concerned the war was over. They had more internal troubles, which probably caused more bloodshed than ever. Captains and officers on two Russian warships stationed at Archangel had been murdered by their crews.

The remaining British troops and authorities were all rapidly leaving, so the country was in chaos. The people were dejected and uncertain as to their future.

The *Asiatic Prince* left Archangel for the last time about the middle of November 1917, passing out of the White Sea along the coast to round the North Cape into the fjords, eventually taking the pilots aboard for the inland passage. The nights were dark and long; and steering had to be by the stars and any outstanding headland that could be distinguished in the black darkness caused by the nearness of the sheer high land on each side of the ship.

They could not make Bergen in daylight, so had to cruise around in the narrow fjord on the approach to this port. Several times the Captain had all hands out with the deep sea hand lead to try to find bottom for an anchorage. A fourteen pound lead was taken on the forecastle head on the ship and the lead line attached was laid along the deck. Men were stationed in a line along the bulwarks about thirty feet apart, each gathering a good-sized coil of the lead line, as the line was capable of reaching one hundred fathoms if the lead was heavy enough. As soon as the lead was dropped into the water the man shouted, 'Watch there, watch,' so when it reached the second man he would allow his coil to run out to feel for bottom and so on until all the line had been run out by each man. If no bottom had been detected the last man with coil would shout, 'No bottom at a hundred fathoms.' Then came some hand pulling to get the lead back again.

The ship just had to keep moving sufficiently to keep her off the shore, but nobody could relax.

They went into Bergen next morning and just saw the tail end of a convoy of ships leaving for Lerwick. These convoys left each morning when the number of ships reached five or six. A Naval officer took over as commodore of the convoy, but he had to join as a civilian, being in neutral waters. When out of sight of land a destroyer escort took over the protection of the ships.

The *Asiatic Prince* was lucky in not catching that convoy. She had to go into port, land her pilots and stay there until next morning, but the convoy which had left was attacked by two German cruisers, which sank all, including the destroyer *Mary Rose*.

There was a great loss of life, as the ships were sunk by heavy gun-fire. Passengers and crews who could, jumped into the sea, hoping to be picked up, but no one was saved.

The *Asiatic Prince* went across with the next convoy without any incidents, and after Lerwick she proceeded to Aberdeen to land passengers and mail.

On that last voyage to Archangel, while coming to anchor, she had run over some sunken object, which caused considerable damage to the ship's bottom. The double-bottomed tanks in numbers one and two holds immediately filled with water, showing that the plating had been opened to the sea. Nothing could be done about it at that port, but as the tank tops held tight it was left until arrival in home waters.

After Aberdeen the ship was ordered to the river Tyne, where they proceeded with a trawler escort. On arrival there the ship was immediately put into dry dock for repairs, and it was found that a great deal of the bottom plating had been set up and the floor stiffeners severely damaged.

After a week in dry dock Tom's indentures were completed, he having done his four years, which qualified him to take the examination for Second Mate. It was rather a coincidence that he had started his apprenticeship in the river Tyne and completed it in practically the same place, and yet had never been there in between times. That four years had worked wonders with Tom. He was self-reliant now with much experience in the ways of the sea. It had been time well spent, and he had no regrets; in fact, he had been happy to be with such good chaps as his fellow apprentices.

Tom had studied hard, which he had to do if he desired to be a responsible officer. He would sooner read a text book on navigation or seamanship than any other type of literature, and he surprised himself in his keenness to learn his future calling. Occasionally the Second or Third Officers would assist him, but they had plenty of work to do and their time was limited.

Mathematics and navigation were subjects which he had to learn entirely on his own, and grab a chance whenever things were quiet to get down to study. Fortunately Tom was with other boys with the same ideas, so they helped each other. One would take the seamanship book in the evenings and with the aid of home-made models and a compass card question the others on the rule of the road at sea, and numerous other seamanship questions. Tom had learned all his articles on this subject whilst lying on his back after falling down the deep tank on the *Ocean Prince* – all thirty-one of them. With navigation problems they plodded along in the usual way, but were more than interested, as they knew that if they did not pass their 2nd Mate examination, it was the forecastle for them. Money – they were all the same – they never had much at any time, so what they never had they never missed. It is often said that apprentices were cheap labour; that may be so, but a boy had more opportunity of obtaining his certificate with other boys of the same character. They worked hard, and prided themselves in knowing the job as a seaman.

If a man fell sick in the engine-room or stoke-hold, or even in the catering department, an apprentice had to fill the gap, so they gained knowledge of every man's job in course of time. An apprentice will some day be Master of his ship, and this knowledge of all departments is indispensable to understanding the men under his command. In narrow waters, canals, rivers and channels, entering and leaving port, the Captain always has the senior apprentice at the helm, and the 2nd senior to stand by him to take over if necessary; that is the way they were taught to take responsibility. In the passages up and down the fjords, Tom spent so much time at the helm that his ankles would swell and had to be bathed in hot water afterwards.

The next move in Tom's life was to report to the owners' office in Newcastle-on-Tyne. In his indentures it was mentioned that at the completion of four years he was to receive five pounds if his reports from the various Masters he had sailed under were good. On arriving at the office he was interviewed by three gentlemen in morning suits who questioned him very closely as if they were very reluctant to hand over the five pounds. Much to Tom's surprise the old white-bearded Superintendent had gone and there was a very keen-eyed gentleman in his place. In the end he got his gratuity for good behaviour.

With his indentures in his pocket he felt free, but very lonely, as the future appeared so uncertain. The war did not seem to have any ending and he was only allowed two months ashore to obtain his certificate.

He signed in at the Navigation School at South Shields to do some schooling. After about six weeks of expert tuition he reported to the examination authorities with his indentures and character report from the owners of the Prince Line. This was a few days before the examination week. His papers had to be scrutinised and checked, and he had to produce a certificate for having passed in first aid work. This was obtained while at the school. All being correct, Tom was told to report at the examination rooms in Sunderland on the following Monday at 9 a.m.

When the time arrived Tom reported as requested. He was feeling highly confident, for at last he was going to be examined. The examiners were Captains Forrest and Robson, and the examination papers all came from the Board of Trade in London.

There must have been about twenty candidates. The papers were given out and all had time limits, so they went ahead at their respective desks. When finished the papers were collected by the examiners who marked them, and the next morning those who had not done well enough were given their service papers back and told to return some other week when they knew their subjects. Tom was always glad when he could carry on each day as he then knew he had satisfied the examiners so far. The paper work was completed on the Friday morning and next came seamanship orals, then he met the examiner face to face and was tested on the rule of the road at sea, the docking of ships and even asked some sailing ship questions, such as how would one get off a lee shore in a gale of wind, wearing ship and the various rigs. Tom got the fright of his life on the very last question, which was about the standing lug sail of a lifeboat. He had been answering questions all day, and had also been tested on his knowledge of visual signalling, and what with that and being nearly at the end of it all his brain went blank, so that on being asked one of the simplest questions of all he could not even think.

It was Friday about 5 p.m. when both the examiners consulted each other and Tom heard one say, 'Either pass him or fail him,' and the other said, 'He has done very well in his work.' In the end Tom was told to come back in the morning, with the admonition that he would not get that chance again.

Next morning Tom was face to face with the examiner once more and all he asked was, 'Do you know now?' Did he know? He knew every sail that was to be known, so he said 'Yes' and with that he was handed his receipt for his certificate which he would collect from the Superintendent at the Board of Trade offices in a few days' time. He had passed. Closing the door behind him he ran all the way to the railway station in case the examiner decided to call him back and take it off him.

He was on the first rung of the ladder now, for he was an officer. He felt so elated that he nearly wept. His parents were delighted too, and so were his brother and sisters.

Now with his 2nd Mate certificate in his hand he applied to his Company for a 3rd Officer's berth; failing a berth there he would have to join the Merchant Shipping Pool and be sent to any old ship, so he thought that he might as well try his old Company, the Prince Line. They came back with a letter informing him that he was to present himself before the Royal Navy Control in Newcastle with a view to attending a gunnery course. He was put on the Prince Line's regular sea-going staff.

Tom duly appeared before the above authority and was given instructions to report to Chatham Barracks, also receiving a first-class railway warrant to travel there, and to appear in uniform, which he did. On arriving at the Chatham Naval Headquarters he reported at the entrance and asked for the Merchant Navy gunnery course. The petty officer at the gate said that he had never heard of it, but he sent a naval boy with Tom to the petty officers' mess to see if they knew anything about such a gunnery course. Nobody there did, so they went to the officers' mess and there he was accepted immediately and joined a class of Merchant Service Officers already there. He was fixed up with accommodation, enjoyed a very nice meal, and felt he had arrived. He was wearing a new uniform with one stripe on the sleeve, feeling awfully new himself as he was only nineteen years old and just out of the half deck. He attended lectures on gunnery, signalling and submarine warfare, also a paravane course, for which he had to go to Portsmouth. It was a good break for Tom to be among the officers. At Chatham he had instructions in all the actions of gun drill, and had a day at sea on firing practice with a 12-pounder gun. The whole course took fifteen days.

Chapter 5

A BRAND-NEW UNIFORM was called for, with a gold stripe on each sleeve, and when he had received it from the tailor he set off for Hull and soon found the docks and the berth in which the *Merchant Prince* was lying. On boarding he reported to the Captain and the steward took him to his cabin. Tom was delighted to have his own cabin, with all the necessary furniture for his comfort. It was not very large, but it was his during the time he would be serving on this ship.

He stowed away his gear, and considered that he had arrived. This was late in January 1918. In the officers' alleyway was the Chief Officer's berth, the Second Officer's and the Third Officer's, and then the bathroom, etc. Tom knew the Chief, Mr Pearson, as he had been Third Officer on the *Portuguese Prince* and Second Officer on the *Asiatic Prince*, so now he was shipmates with him again, and a fine man he was. The Second Officer, John Stonehouse, was a long, skinny man, but full of dry humour, so Tom looked forward to a happy period on the *Merchant Prince*.

The ship was discharging cargo from Mediterranean ports. After that was out and the crew signed on, she left Hull for London, arriving there in a day or so. Tom had the eight to twelve watch morning and night, and on the coast the Captain was there on the bridge with him.

When the cargo was loading the Third and Second Officers supervised the forward and after holds respectively. They were also duty officers every other night, so they could not be on shore together. When Tom wanted to stretch his legs on shore the Fourth Engineer made good company.

After completing loading at London – all war cargo for Malta and Alexandria – the ship proceeded to Falmouth to make up a convoy with ships coming from the west coast ports. While there, the ship's lifeboats were put into the water for boat drill under the supervision of a Naval officer. All the crew were sent away with Tom in one boat and the Second in the other boat, to practise sailing and oar pulling. The boats were then hoisted on board and slung outboard ready for any emergency at sea.

The *Merchant Prince* was usually Commodore ship, meaning that the Naval Commodore and his staff operated from her, as she had extra tall masts for signalling and spare accommodation for staff. She was painted

SS *Merchant Prince.*

in camouflage colours, as were all ships then, which altered the appearance of a vessel when seen from a distance.

The convoy sailed with about forty ships, each having a number indicated by a two flag signal hoist from the Allied signal manual. All captains had assembled ashore for instructions from the Commodore before sailing, so they knew their number and station. Three destroyers were the usual escort.

As they sailed out of port in single line, the Commodore ship first, they looked a never-ending stream of ships. The signal would be given and all ships formed up in the pre-arranged plan, in columns of six or seven. Their initial number indicated the column each ship had to be in and the second the number in that column. They soon formed up and proceeded at about seven and a half knots, taking their station from the Commodore ship which was leading the middle column. The escorts lay well out ahead and on the beam both sides, listening for underwater craft on their asdic gear.

The first stop was Gibraltar, to make a fresh convoy with another Commodore and staff. This one would go as far as Bizerta on the North African coast. The next stretch was to Malta, and ships going there would break off, while the convoy proceeded to Alexandria. When completed at Malta the ship would join the next passing convoy to Alexandria.

With all this convoy work Tom was gaining experience in sailing with ships in close company. In time they made Alexandria, and discharged the cargo for there. Homewards the same procedure was operated in reverse.

Tom was acting gunnery officer on this ship. She had a 4.7 gun on the poop, with three Naval gunners, while part of the crew made up the loaders. Much practice was taken with the gun so all were in good shape.

Nothing much happened to the *Merchant Prince* while Tom served on her, but he gained a lot of good experience as an officer, especially when convoys were on a zig-zag course.

When zig-zagging, a special clock was used on the navigating bridge. This was an electric clock, with stops on the outside edge. They were clamped in place on the times the course had to be altered. These times varied so as not to give a target to any submarine working for a position to fire torpedoes at any particular vessel they hoped to sink with a square-on torpedo, bearing in mind that the torpedo had to hit square on the nose to explode. The large hand of the clock had a thin piece of metal at its tip. On touching, the stopper would make an electrical contact, which would cause a buzzing noise. This indicated that the course had to be altered according to the zig-zag track the convoy was making, which was never the same on each turn.

The convoy turned and moved like a company of soldiers, the ships on the inner side slowing down and those on the outside moving faster to keep in line abeam. This was happening about ten times in the hour and with never the same interval. Torpedoes had been seen skimming through the water without striking a target. Ships kept station two cables on the beam and two cables astern of each other in the column, and a large convoy would cover a very large area of seawater. In cases like this, the destroyers of the escort would dash through the convoy to spot a submarine, dropping depth charges which could force such a craft to the surface where it could be disposed of. It was the escorts' duty to keep clear of the merchant ships when inside the convoy, as some confusion would have been caused if all tried to keep clear of each other.

Officers when taking the gunnery course always had instruction in convoy work, so all knew what the drill was. Clocks on all ships in the convoy were checked each day at 1 p.m. by a Time Ball from the Commodore ship, so that all ships would move at exactly the same time. In those days there was no radio check for the chronometers. Chronometers were checked in port by the Time Ball generally mounted on top of a convenient hill or the harbourmaster's office. Some ports had a gun fired at 1 p.m., because this was usually the time for Time Balls as well.

Malta harbour was always full of HM ships, so the town of Valletta had swarms of Navy men milling about and destroyers were constantly dashing in or out of harbour. At night morse lamps were blinking out messages from each ship, large or small. They had no fear of air raids in those days. The Maltese bum boats and gondolas were making their fortunes out of the seamen. Ashore too, the honky tonks were raking the ships in and keeping the boys happy. The Maltese thrived on the Navy, so much so that their lives depended on such activities. A good percentage of young men from that island joined the Navy as stewards, and it was more Naval than the dockyard towns of Devonport and Portsmouth.

At Alexandria in Egypt, the British Army spread itself all over the city, with a minor smattering of the Navy for good measure. There, too, the locals made fortunes out of the Services, even the garbage boats, which were owned and manned by Egyptians, in their good office of collecting the rubbish from ships of war. Money was plentiful for those local gentlemen attending on the Armed Forces.

Tom Sloane, Third Officer of the SS *Merchant Prince*, was a ringside spectator to all this. But war is war anywhere. Men make fortunes and men die fighting.

Tom's third voyage was in an extra large convoy from the Channel and UK ports in which the *Merchant Prince* was the Commodore ship. Approaching Gibraltar ships were forming into two columns to go into Gibraltar Bay when a few shots were fired at some suspicious object by one of the escorts, just to remind folk that a war was still in being. When all ships were told to act independently approaching the anchorage, the *Merchant Prince* went in close to the breakwater mole to discharge the Commodore and his staff, and a pilot boarded with the remark to the Captain that the war would be over in half an hour. Tom Sloane was all ears as he was on the bridge, handling the engine telegraphs. The date was 11 November 1918, and when the half-hour was up it was 11 a.m. As the ship was close to the mole at anchor she was in range for seeing the sights on shore, including the warships lying on the inboard side of the mole. Men came streaming down the gangways on to the mole and marched up and down shouting, 'The war is over!' Bands were playing, and whistles of ships were blowing. There was no mistaking that great events were happening and that the war had stopped for some reason or other. No one had thought about an armistice, which later was proclaimed to all.

The Captain of the *Merchant Prince* thought the occasion was appropriate for calling his officers into his cabin to join him in toasting the event. Glasses were procured and a little drop was poured into the Chief's and Second's glasses, while the contents of a bottle of lemonade was poured into the Third Officer's. Tom felt like saying, 'Well, where do we go from here?'

An American ship, the *Iona*, loaded with ammunition, was lying about a couple of cables from the *Merchant Prince*. The crew were having high jinks firing rockets and had apparently fired some down the hold ventilators. In no time she was on fire, and all kinds of explosions were going off. The *Merchant Prince* was shifted out of her range, because of the high explosives. Calls for the tugs went out by signals on the siren from the *Iona*, as being where she was she would have burned the whole dockyard out.

The crew managed to swim to the shore, which was not far away. Tom understood that one man got stuck in a port in trying to get out, as everywhere else was burning fiercely. The tugs did valiant work in putting wires aboard over the stern for towing her out of the close proximity of the dockyard. Another explosion blew the windlass off the forecastle, still with the anchor chains attached, so she was stretched to the utmost of her cables and kept there until she burned down. The whole ship was white-hot; the man in the porthole could not get out, he died.

On the *Merchant Prince* the Fourth Engineer also died. He had the so-called 'Spanish 'flu' and should have been taken ashore to hospital. The 'flu came upon him so suddenly that all were astounded when he died so quickly. He was buried in Gibraltar cemetery, and most of the crew attended as the ship was lying off at anchor. The best the ship could do, including his shipmates, was done. It was a very sad affair, as he was a particular friend of Tom's.

The Admiralty was sending out messages to all German submarines to give themselves up as the war was over, and several came into Gibraltar and surrendered.

After a while the *Merchant Prince* was allowed to proceed on her way to Malta alone. It seemed strange not being in convoy. Eventually the ship arrived at Malta and then sailed on to Alexandria. She loaded bales of cotton in the holds and onions on deck to the height of the navigating bridge. Arriving in Hull the ship lay on the inside of a wharf, the other side being the riverside. There Tom watched the cross-Channel boats bringing in British soldiers who had been prisoners of war in Germany. Many pathetic sights were seen as mothers and wives of soldiers who were missing were at the foot of the gangway as the men came down, asking about their menfolk.

At Hull another Captain joined the ship. He had been in captivity in enemy territory for two years. The Captain who was relieved was going out to Egypt to marry a girl he had been courting. She had been on the ship at Alexandria, and next voyage Tom met him again, as he was Harbourmaster at Jaffa where the ship was discharging. That is one way to gain a Harbourmaster's job.

Chapter 6

IN APRIL 1919 Tom left the *Merchant Prince* to go and polish up his studies for a First Mate's certificate, and then to present himself for examination. He signed in at the school again, and after the first week he suddenly decided to put his papers in to the Board of Trade for inspection in order to sit the examination. He had studied hard on the *Merchant Prince* and felt very confident.

Twelve months' sea time in charge of a watch was the interval between gaining a Second Mate's certificate and being examined for a First Mate's. Tom had completed fifteen months sea time on the *Merchant Prince* and his papers were in order, so he sat this examination at South Shields on his second week ashore.

Good fortune came his way again as he passed first time, so now he had a brand-new First Mate's ticket. After allowing himself a month's holiday the time came to find another ship, and the company offered him the *Arabian Prince*, as Third Officer again. Tom accepted and joined her at Hull, where she was discharging a cargo of grain from the River Plate ports. She was a good-sized cargo ship for those days, about nine thousand tons deadweight, having just completed her maiden voyage of about four months, so she was practically a new ship.

The *Arabian Prince* was a ship which was very suitable for the River Plate trade, as she was very lightly constructed in the holds, having a portable wooden bulkhead at the after end of number two hold and the same down the centre of number three hold, which did not give very much stiffening in the amidship area. Having no deep tanks for water ballast on light ship passages, only the double bottoms were used for water ballast, and the bunker coal only used the after compartment of number three wooden bulkhead. This was typical for a River Plate tramp, when as much cargo as possible could be loaded, but bunker coal could be replenished at St Vincent Island, halfway on the voyage homewards.

Being so lightly constructed made her tremble like a jelly on a light passage, so that it was impossible to do any writing at all in the chartroom, which with the navigating bridge, high above the main deck, was on a level with the funnel top.

The Captain, who had been in the ship since she left the shipyard, knew her defects, so asked for solid ballast to take her across to New York after the cargo was out, and for this purpose she went to Middlesbrough to take solid ballast of slag from the steelworks.

While there, Tom received a cheque from the owners for thirty-six pounds, being a gratuity for war service. Apparently all war-time servants received such a cheque, varying in amount according to the rank held, and Tom's cheque was like manna from Heaven, for he was completely broke after being ashore so long, so he made sure it was nicely laid away in the local bank.

Eventually the ship left Middlesbrough for New York to load for the Far East. She docked at the company's usual berth, and Tom was amazed at the change in that area since he had last been there at the beginning of the war. Where green fields once were it was now all built up, and this did not improve the outlook by any means, as new property soon took on the appearance of the old.

New buildings were springing up like mushrooms over at Manhattan, old ones being demolished in the process, and new offices and industry would soon blot out the pleasant scenery which Tom had had the good fortune to see in the New York of before the war.

The ship loaded a full cargo, about half being case oil for the lamps of China. The fore part of number three hold between the wooden bulkhead

SS *Arabian Prince.*

of the after end of number two hold and the wooden bulkhead separating the bunker coal down the centre of number three hold was stowed with this case oil which was in wooden boxes each containing two two-gallon tins of kerosene or lamp oil. It also occupied the lower holds of numbers one, four and five holds.

The rest of the cargo consisted of all kinds of miscellaneous goods, including steel rails for Singapore. About three hundred tons of bunker coal was taken over number three hatch on deck as there was no room in the bunker space. The ship was bound for Aden, Singapore, Manila, Swatow, China, and Hong Kong with this cargo.

She sailed about the end of July in the hot summer of New York, and trailed her way leisurely at about ten and a half knots towards the Mediterranean Sea and Port Said for the Suez Canal.

About four days out from New York, the Chief Engineer reported that a crack had developed in the main propeller shaft. The ship was stopped to see what could be done, and as a temporary repair one of the bearings was moved over the crack, then the Captain decided to steer towards the Azores at very slow speed. A wireless message was sent off to the owners. Ponta Delgado was the port to make for, and fortunately the weather was fine, the sea as smooth as a billiard table.

It took them many days to reach the port at about three and a half knots, and on arrival there the *Arabian Prince* anchored in the good-sized bay on the southern coast of San Miguel Island.

Close by was a United States ship, which was later found to be the USS *Buffalo*, a repair ship. She was anchored here as a halfway unit between the Mediterranean and the United States for repairs to small craft such as destroyers and merchant ships of the United States making the voyage across the Atlantic.

At this port there was only a Lloyd's agent. The American officers must have been curious as to why the ship had anchored in this bay, so they came on board at the Lloyd's agent's invitation to look over the damaged shaft and give an opinion, as their ship would have many repair facilities to offer, together with trained craftsmen.

They wished to repair the shaft by welding and were given permission to have a go, so the *Arabian Prince* tied up alongside the USS *Buffalo*. The shaft was about two feet in diameter, so it was quite a big task, and if successful would be one of the biggest welding jobs ever done.

The Americans rigged up all their own gear, such as lighting and whatever was needed. The crack was cut down in a 'V' shape to allow the welding to get well into the break. This was done by hand tools, men relieving each other on the cutting. When the 'V' had been cut down all round, the welding commenced. The time taken to complete the work was just over six weeks, and when the welding was finished they filed off all the ragged ends, which gave an excellent finish to the work.

The next thing was to have sea trials to test the work done, so the *Arabian Prince* cast off the USS *Buffalo* and moved out of port. All the Americans who had been working on the shaft came out with the ship to inspect the repair work while the ship was put full speed ahead and astern, then ran some distance before returning to port The Americans seemed very satisfied with the work, and Tom heard them say to the Captain before leaving that the shaft would take the ship out to China and back again.

With this in mind he must have sailed away at full speed with a satisfied feeling, but the ship had only just dropped the island from view when the Chief Engineer came up on the bridge to inform the Captain that the welding was dropping out of the cracked shaft, so he had to turn the ship back and at dead slow speed reached Ponta Delgado again.

The American officers came on board and had the *Arabian Prince* moored alongside the *Buffalo* once more, and in a short time they had fitted a steel clamp over the shaft, after which the *Arabian Prince* proceeded to Gibraltar at slow speed, reaching there after several days at sea.

The ship was now two months late on her journey. On arrival at Gibraltar Lloyd's surveyor boarded her, and it was decided to fit a new shaft, which was coming out from England. There was no entry into the shaft tunnel from the engine room, while the steel bulkhead could not be cut to allow the new shaft to enter on account of the inflammable cargo of case oil in the hold.

Number four hold had to be discharged of this oil in order to get at the tunnel to take off some plates to allow the new shaft to be shipped. This all took time and the ship was now several months delayed on her voyage, which caused other serious worries.

While the shore gangs were discharging number four hold, smoke was detected coming out of the ventilators at number three hold, which indicated a fire somewhere in that hold. The Captain ordered all ventilation to be blocked off to the hold, and the officers and crew were all employed covering up ventilators and all outlets to the compartment. The hatch was lifted on the cargo side and volumes of smoke came out, so that was securely battened down. All coal had to be shifted off the hatch, and all turned to with shovels to move it off and pile it up on each side. The coal on deck was a headache at any time.

As the ship was anchored close to the mole she was towed further out into deep water. The tug then put fire hoses on board down the hatch on both sides of the amidship wooden bulkhead. The tarpaulins were secured around the hoses so that no air was allowed in the hold.

A good head of water was pumped into the hold until such time as there was fear of the ship sinking. Then the pumping was stopped and the ship was towed over to the beach at the head of the bay and beached on Spanish soil.

The pumping recommenced, then it was found that the stokehold bulkhead, being of steel at the fore side of the stokehold, was bulging badly with the possibility of bursting.

The Second Officer, together with Tom and the crew, made to shore the bulkhead at the bulge, but could find no place to shore it to except the boiler ends. With hatch timber and such-like they did shore the bulkhead to the boiler ends, although these were not a good place to shore to.

Shortly after this, while still completing their work, a rumbling noise was heard on the other side of the bulkhead, and then an explosion, and all the shores dropped down on the stokehold plates and the bulge went back into place. The explosion had blown all the hatches off the hold and the compressed gas escaped, which was the end of the fire. Apparently with all air being shut off from the hold, and the tug pumping water in at a terrific rate, the gases in the hold were being highly compressed, which was causing the bulkhead to bulge in the stokehold which had just been shored, and so found its way out by the explosion, blowing the hatches off the top. Although there were hatches on in the 'tween deck and caulked with oakum and cargo on top of that, all of these had been ripped out by the explosion upwards, and it was a mercy the bulkhead did not burst. In pumping the water to kill the fire, wherever it was, water had filled up both number three lower hold and number two lower hold, as owing to the division bulkhead being of wood and portable it was not watertight by any means. Number two lower hold was full of highly expensive general cargo.

After consultations with Lloyd's and the Naval authorities, the ship was pumped out by three tugs. When the water was out, the ship lifted off the bottom and came off the beach under tow, then she was taken to the inside of the mole and made fast there.

By then the company's Superintendent, London salvage surveyors and Lloyd's surveyors were all on the job. All cargo had to be discharged from number two hold in order to ascertain the damage and have it put right or the cargo sold by auction if it was of any value. Number three hold had to be entirely discharged and emptied of coal and case oil.

Tom was put in charge of number two hold and, with a gang of shore workers, had to tally each article out of the hold. All the cargo was damaged by sea water, and some cases would not hold together because the nails had come out. On some, the marks had been nearly obliterated and so were hard to decipher. Cases and bags of perishables were in a rotten state, were just hoisted out of the hold and taken away to be destroyed. Heavy machinery was cleaned up and put in good order, the Salvage Surveyor examining every article to decide what was to be done with it. This was hard, dirty work and the atmosphere was rank due to the effect of the cargo being contaminated by the sea water.

One of the local men, working under Tom's direction, always presented him with a cigar every morning before starting the day's work, with dignified courtesy. It was noticed that a large bale of cotton goods on the 'tween deck above was resting on the coaming on its outer edge, the bulk of the bale being inboard. As the men were filling the net sling with boxes, etc., Tom was leaning over to find the marking on them, just below this bale. The ship was given a list, but Tom did not notice it as he was so intent on his work. Before the sling was hove up, his friend with the cigars was helping Tom occasionally when a case had to be turned over to find its identification marking. Tom was speaking to the man, and, turning his head away for a moment, looked back and was surprised to find him stretched out flat on his back, and shocked to the extreme to find him stone dead with a large bale lying beside him.

The listing of the ship had been so great that the bale above had fallen out of the 'tween deck, striking the man on the forehead and killing him outright. Tom was only inches away from him, yet no noise or any disturbance had occurred to warn him of this happening. Apparently some engine room tank was filled to give the ship a list for reasons unknown.

Later in the day Tom was called out of the hatch in a hurry as there had been an accident at number three hatch. He rushed to the scene and found the Second Officer trying to stop the bleeding on a man's thigh, which had been trapped in the steam winch as the man leaned over it when it was moving. The Second Officer was covered in blood, and he and Tom both endeavoured to stop the bleeding. Before the ambulance came they had to bandage the thigh tightly, and as the wound was so big they turned his leg up from the knee and lashed it. The Second Officer had used part of his shirt to make a tourniquet, tightening it with a stick as a Spanish windlass. The man died, however, soon after he had been received into the hospital.

The Second Officer and Tom attended these men's funerals and gave condolences to their families. The whole business was trying to all, and most depressing.

After number three hold had been discharged of the bunker coal it was found that through spontaneous combustion a great hole had been burned through the wooden divisional bulkhead, big enough to drive a horse and cart through. The amazing sight, though, was to see the case oil tins on the other side of the hole, standing as stowed, while all wooden cases had been charred to nothing, but there was not a drop of kerosene in the tins. This suggests that the sealing of the hatch against the inlet of air was successful, otherwise the blaze would have engulfed the whole ship.

In time the cargo that could be restored was returned to the hold, and the ship was made seaworthy again. The new shaft was fitted and number four hold re-stowed. After the vessel's unhappy time she proceeded on her voyage to the Far East, and more coal was shipped over number three hatch at Malta. The stuff was with them in their meals and in every nook and cranny. In the engine room they suffered no better, as they had the ash dust all over the engines, and when the tropics were approached the heat was terrific down in that department.

On arriving at Port Said the Canal pilot boarded with all his usual pomp, together with his two Arab servants. He cast a baleful eye over the coal on deck amidships and remarked that he must have the hose playing water on the coal to keep the dust down.

After passing through the Canal the first port of call was Aden, to discharge the cargo for that port. Both the Second Officer and Tom took tally of each case or package that went out, as many claims would be made by the consignee on the mere fact of the nature of the 'General Average' insurance that was placed on all cargo, to assist in paying for the delay and misfortunes.

The next stop was Sabang, a small island to the north of Sumatra, where bunkers were taken again, as the coal had been worked well down on the long passage out. There the junior engineers had to tally the coal on board; it came in small baskets, which the numerous workers carried on their heads.

The following stop was Singapore, where a considerable amount of cargo was taken out while the ship was lying in the stream. The steel railway lines were discharged into lighters. The workers here were Indian on the ship and Chinese in the lighters.

Completing there, the ship made for Manila and soon only the case oil remained, this being bound for Swatow in Southern China.

The weather was very hot now, and the engine room was hotter, and Tom had much sympathy for the engineers, who were so wet with the sweat from their bodies that they could not have been wetter if they had fallen overboard.

At Swatow a Chinese pilot took the ship into port and to the oil storage wharf. The Chinese workers seemed to be a strong, sturdy set of men. As it was the month of December, it was extremely cold at sundown and through the nights but fine and warm when the sun was up. The latitude was about twenty-three degrees north.

A painting of SS *Arabian Prince* by Bruce Clark.

When completed at Swatow they proceeded to Hong Kong for dry-docking, the ship now being empty of cargo, so that she shook like a jelly when under way at sea, and trying to work a sight up or even writing the log book was impossible. An outsider could say with confidence, after viewing any writing done under such circumstances, that the writer must have been under the influence of alcohol.

A few days were spent in Hong Kong tied up to buoys waiting for cargo. The Radio Officer and Tom would go on shore after being taken from the ship on a sampan, which was a small boat manned by one person facing the bow of the boat and plying the oars by pushing instead of pulling.

This being Tom's first time in these waters everything was new to him, as well as to the Radio Officer. They wandered up the hillside and watched the natives working away at their numerous trades and skills well into the nights. There were coppersmiths, blacksmiths, tinsmiths, bootmakers, tailors, little shops selling native foods and Chinese women clacking on the pavements with the wooden soles of their shoes. And always there was that tap tap in some sort of rhythm caused by a youth tapping two hardwood sticks together as he walked aimlessly along the road.

The night was lit up by flaring and spluttering kerosene flares, the lamps of China, over the industrial smiths and outside the mysterious alcoves and shops which were doing business at all hours of the night. Work stopped with those people only when the customers ceased to come in, or with the smith when at last he could not see and just lay down and slept beside his workshop fire.

The young men found it interesting that they were greeted by friendly smiles, but after that no notice was taken of them. They just walked among the people as two of the community.

Hong Kong is an island, the town at the waterfront facing Kowloon. About five miles across the water on the mainland is Victoria where all the main shipping interests are carried on. From there the island rises to a peak some two thousand feet high. A railway ran up this steep incline, but the carriages up and down were manipulated by being attached to a heavy wire connected to a winding machine at the top, and as one set went up the other set was being lowered.

It was a great thrill to Tom to go on this railway and see the harbour down below, as well as being able to view the wonderful scenery on the passage up and down. Many fine homes were built on the mountainside, with roads to them, and at night the lighting showed up like a fairy picture.

There was much of interest going on around the ship. Junks came alongside with cargo. Two or three families would be on one craft, with children and grandparents as well as dogs. The women appeared to do all the work, looking after the children and handling sails or oars, with the grandmother doing the cooking. These people never lived on shore, and it was said that a quarter of the population of China lived afloat.

The ship left for Singapore and there loaded baled rubber for New York. Tom heard that this was the only cargo she could take, as she had not made a good name for herself with the trouble on the voyage out. The *Arabian Prince* took practically a full cargo from Singapore. Much rubber was available then just after the war, as stocks had mounted up. Also, the motor car industry was expanding fast.

Following an uneventful passage to New York via the Suez Canal, the ship arrived after a voyage of ten months, which was twice as long as a ship should have taken.

When the cargo had been discharged she waited some time for another one, and eventually took a full load of coal to le Havre in France. A change of captains had been made in New York, and Tom was pleased to find that the new Captain was a friendlier man. At le Havre the Captain went home and got married, returning with his bride, and the ship then went back to New York.

On arriving there she was on the berth to load for the Levant. This cargo was similar to a Red Cross contribution to the distressed people of Greece and to the Russian refugees who could be reached from Istanbul. This was from the United States relief organisation. The ship loaded a full cargo of foodstuff in which was about two thousand tons of bagged flour. Indeed, everything possible was included for the relief of the distressed.

When loaded, the ship proceeded on her way, the first port being Piraeus in Greece. In due course she arrived there, and about half of the cargo was discharged. There Tom took the opportunity to visit Athens and its ancient monuments during a day off duty.

Then on to Istanbul (Constantinople). They passed up through the Aegean Sea to the Dardanelles, where the Allied war graves could plainly be seen, and on through the Sea of Marmara to Istanbul. It was a most interesting voyage.

The ship anchored just below the bridge. The waters around were packed with small boats, from tugs to small rowing boats, and on these were living families of the White Russian refugees. It was believed they were mostly of the upper classes of old Russia, and to make their troubles worse they were not allowed to land.

Tom looked upon this fleet with great sympathy, as no humans should suffer as they did. The ship had about four thousand tons of foodstuff for this port, but whether any of it got to these people is doubtful.

Many boats came alongside at nights begging for food, so the Second Officer and Tom defied all rules and regulations, opened up a hatch and passed down bags of flour and other goods. I daresay that is the way the Americans, who had given this cargo, intended it to be distributed. Women and children in a starving condition can be very appealing.

The British Navy were stationed here and they were under their protection. It was always a welcome sight in any foreign port to see a huge British battleship.

The SS *Arabian Prince*, not being alongside any wharf, discharged the cargo into lighters, and when empty she proceeded to Alexandria. At that port the whole of number three lower hold was being used for bunker coal. This was divided from the cargo hold number two by the wooden bulkhead mentioned previously.

Again they had trouble with the bunker coal through spontaneous combustion. The coal towards the wooden bulkhead was very hot, so it was decided to take the coal out. The local labour started to discharge it, but after a while it was found to be really on fire, so Tom got the job of seeing that the hoses were playing water over it to cool it down. This process had to go on all the time until the coal was out.

The ship was loading a full cargo of cotton in bales for Boston. This needed special precautions against fire, so the bulkhead in question was lined with asbestos sheets on both sides. New coal was taken, just enough to see the ship back to New York where she would go after Boston

When a ship was on the berth to take cotton the number of bales loaded each day depended on the buying of the cotton at the cotton exchange, and the amounts varied each day.

In due course the ship was loaded, re-bunkered and ready to go, so off she went to Boston, USA. Tom was still Third Officer, but a very experienced one now, and he wrote to the company to ensure that he would not be overlooked for promotion to Second Officer. The present Second Officer had an Extra Master's certificate and had been four years in the Royal Navy. He was a keen navigator, and from him Tom learned quite a lot of useful knowledge. The Second Officer and Tom took solar, stellar and lunar observations when the opportunities occurred, even to correcting the chronometers at sea by these means. Tom's studies were also scrutinised by this officer. The ship had been out of the United Kingdom for fifteen months, and the Board of Trade regulations demanded twelve months' sea service as Second Officer before he could present himself to be examined for a Master's certificate. With this in mind Tom decided it was about time he was promoted.

Chapter 7

O N ARRIVING BACK IN NEW YORK after discharging all cargo at Boston, the Second Officer was promoted to Chief Officer on another ship, which was on the New York-Santos coffee trade. Tom was promoted to Second Officer in his place on the *Arabian Prince*, the date being 17 November 1920.

The new Third Officer had been in the Royal Navy during the war, and was older than Tom. He had obtained his Second Mate's certificate when he was released from the Navy at the end of hostilities, during which he had served as Warrant Officer.

The *Arabian Prince* loaded a full cargo for South African ports and also took the United States mail to Cape Town. The passage south was excellent, with smooth seas and warm weather. Her average speed was the best she had ever done at 10.6 knots, and Tom found he had quite a time-consuming job correcting charts from the Notice to Mariners issued by the Board of Trade which would reach the ship at nearly every port.

As conditions began to settle down to peacetime routine all lights and fog signals on the United Kingdom coasts were being reinstated, but altered from their pre-war characteristics. Much stronger lights were being installed with different flashing periods. Minefields had to be plotted, buoys were being moved about and hundreds lifted altogether. Wrecks were being located and had to be marked on the charts, so that as there were hundreds of those, the charts were becoming crowded with corrections in red ink.

Then there were the cargo plans to make out, each port cargo being identified by different colours to save time in placing labour at ports of discharge. The Third Officer had his hands full, copying all marks and numbers of the cargo in alphabetical order for each port in special tally books.

Not that they grumbled at this work, as it was all part of their duties. All officers took an interest in the navigation of the ship. Each had to take stellar or solar observations on his watch, and the error on the compasses had to be observed and recorded. Only magnetic compasses were the guides of the mariner and the error would alter considerably at each change of course. In foggy weather, when observations could not be taken, they had to fall back on their records tabulated in the compass correction book from previous observations.

The ship duly arrived at Cape Town, twenty-six days after leaving New York. The cargo for that port was soon worked out, so while what Tom saw of Cape Town impressed him very much, he did not have much time to roam around.

The next port was Vassal Bay and then Port Elizabeth. These ports were not protected by breakwaters, so that a ship could only work there in fine weather. The final port was Durban, where the remainder of the cargo was discharged. Tom considered Durban a grand place, as beautiful as the weather. He enjoyed himself in the swimming pools, as it was dangerous to swim off the beaches on account of sharks.

While at Durban the Captain received orders to proceed to the island of Mauritius, Port Louis. A charter had been arranged to load bagged sugar for United Kingdom ports, so the ship was on her way home at last.

Mauritius was reached about the end of January 1921. Some eight ships were lying off the port at anchor, and three or four more were tied up to buoys inside the small inlet, all waiting to load on the same charter as the *Arabian Prince*. Apparently huge stocks of sugar had accumulated through lack of ships to take it away during the war.

Now the ships were here to load the cargo, but it was a slow process, as each ship was taking fifteen days to load with native labour. Tom's ship anchored to take her turn, which was last, and this was not completed till May.

Ships could only anchor in depths of ten fathoms for less than a mile offshore on a ledge. Outside that it was over a thousand fathoms deep, the island being a coral island.

To keep everybody happy they had to do something besides the ordinary day's work. so they put one of the lifeboats into the water, using it as a liberty boat at times, but the main reason was to get some sailing practice in, and they noticed the other ships at anchor doing the same. Eventually this led to challenges to race, but when that was organised it was found that the sails were inadequate for any speed. So a new mast, longer than the original, was constructed to make a suitable mainsail instead of the dipping lug to meet BOT standards; also a foresail and jib were rigged. To take all this sail a keel was fitted about $12'' \times 2\frac{1}{2}''$ about two-thirds of the length of the boat. A few firebars too were placed into the bottom of the hull. With this rig they certainly made a good pace but some of the other ships' boats had two masts and they could not do much against them. So they made a topsail on a yard, which could be hoisted to the top of the mast when running before the wind.

Every Sunday morning they had an official race out in the open sea. A ten-mile course was laid out and marked by paint drums anchored with old firebars in the form of a triangle, so they had the wind from all directions during the course of the race. Generally the Third Officer and Tom took charge with the apprentices for crew; during the week the rest of the crew in off hours played football on an Army pitch ashore. Of course the boat was then used as a liberty boat.

The Sunday morning lifeboat race was terrific — it took all of one's strength and nerve to get the best from the boat, but they were never far behind. In fact they won by a short head once the topsail was produced and they were running back into port. As they came back down by the vessels at anchor every boat was greeted by loud cheers by the ships' companies at the rails. The one and only prize was a bottle of whisky, suitably presented by a Captain's wife on one of the ships. The sailing ship had its boat in the race, but this crew could give it a good race any time.

Sometimes they had a regatta during the week at night-time. All the boats followed each other, led by a Clan Line boat whose Second Officer played the bagpipes. The harbour was so quiet that they could be heard by the residents ashore, and many of these came down to the beach to watch. The rigging on all the boats was dressed with coloured lights, which were hurricane lamps with bunting around them.

Each ship had a football team and matches were played on Wednesday and Saturday afternoon. The *Arabian Prince*'s football colours were made by their singlets being dyed with Dolly Blue. Short pants were come by by cutting down their white uniform trousers. The Captain gave them the ball, which took some inflating.

The British Army had a small garrison on the island, and every week a team would go to their station and play a game and have a social evening, so they saw a different set of men each visit.

The ships were gradually loading and leaving, until the *Arabian Prince* was the only one left outside. This was about the end of March, and cyclones had been reported in the Indian Ocean. An observation station on the hilltop, in the care of monks of one of the religious orders, made the observations.

The warnings were received by the Captain when he was ashore, and he came off one day with the news that a cyclone was approaching the Island. The ship was in no condition to meet a cyclone, for the Chief and Third Officers were both laid up, the First with some special ailment of his own, and the Third with a poisoned wrist from a mosquito bite. The hatches were open as the sailors were painting them out, and the engineers had one boiler open for cleaning purposes.

The anchor was paid out to ninety fathoms of chain, hoping that would hold her, but in two hours from the Captain arriving on board the cyclone overwhelmed the island as well as the ships in Port Louis harbour. The wind and rain struck the *Arabian Prince* like an explosion. That was at 4 p.m., and in no time the ship was out at sea, with ninety fathoms of anchor chain and an anchor hanging over the port bow. The hatches had been battened down, but the engines could not cope with these conditions.

Fortunately, the wind was off the land, which drove the ship out to sea. There was no hope of picking the anchor up, as the windlass could not be approached, and in any case the ship had not sufficient steam. Tom considered the anchor was doing more good hanging so low in the water, as otherwise the ship might have turned over. As it was, she was rolling like a swinging pendulum. The seas were vicious and with a force of wind which could have been well over one hundred miles per hour. The whole ship was engulfed in blinding spray and those aboard were at the mercy of the gods.

Tom Sloane was on the navigating bridge, which, as mentioned before, was about the highest part of the ship. The only reason he was there was because he was supposed to be there when the ship was at sea. At that height the rolling was terrific, so he jammed himself between the engine room telegraph and a voice pipe to the engine room. The ship, being in the direct path of the storm, was carried along with it for some considerable time, suffering the lashings and torment of the wind and sea. When Tom could see the waves through the flying spray they did not look pleasant by any means, for the spray was driving with such force that it was whipping up canvas covers, tarpaulins and boat covers and everything movable, and actually laying bare the steelwork of the ship's construction, removing all paintwork in direct contact with the full force of wind and spray.

The Lord only knows how the ship kept afloat that night, as she was powerless. Next morning early the wind suddenly shifted about ninety degrees. They had no idea how the ship was heading, as the magnetic compasses were completely full of sea water, both the one on the flying bridge and the one in the chartroom, where the cards were floating.

The storm was travelling faster than the ship was being carried along with it. Tom felt that the anchor and its ninety fathoms of chain had something to do with that. The wind then shifted considerably again, with terrific rain storms.

Gradually the wind was losing its high shrieking noise, and by the afternoon of the first full day of the storm the wind had died down but left a tremendous swell on the sea. Still the ship was helpless for power. The engineers worked hard to get steam up on the two boilers capable of steaming. Fires could not be fed when she was in the heart of the cyclone.

The third boiler was made ready, but had no fresh water. Eventually, as the storm moved further away, steam was raised, the compasses emptied of water and the cards dried and balanced on their pivots, and the ship was put on course again after observations had been made for the ship's position. She was about a hundred miles from Port Louis, and it took nearly three days to get back to port and anchor. The ships inside had suffered considerable damage, being tied to buoys with anchor chain on buoy at the stem, and rope and wire moorings at the stern. Apparently they had carried away their stern moorings and so kept into the wind, with the occasional banging against each other.

There were only two steamers in such a fix, however. A sailing ship had been in port but had left a few days before the storm and probably missed it.

During the first two weeks of April 1921 the *Arabian Prince* was loading sugar in bags, for London. Blackwater fever began to affect some of the crew, and two were left in hospital. Two replacements from the same hospital were taken on, so away she went – homeward bound at last. All were glad to see the last of Mauritius.

The ship was trailing along in fine weather at about nine knots. The South African coal which was taken at Durban was poor steaming coal. A few days out, on a hot tropical day with rather a big swell on the sea but otherwise no breaking water, Tom was relaxing on a camp stool on deck before going on the bridge to take a noon sight of the sun for latitude.

One of the deck crew members came along and showed Tom a piece of paper, on which was written that a certain other crew member had left all his effects to this man. The man asked when he could claim the effects. Tom asked him where the man was and the seaman producing the script casually said that he had just jumped over the stern into the sea about ten minutes previously.

Tom immediately shouted to the Captain, 'Man overboard,' and threw a lifebuoy over as a marker. The Captain stopped the ship and ordered the small boat away. It was swung out ready for lowering and Tom had to go away with it, so he picked three men to go along with him to handle the oars. The Chief Officer had the men at the falls and Tom shouted, 'Let go as soon as the swell lifts the boat.' When the order came to let go, the man at the after falls did so, but the joker held on to the forward falls, the result being that when the swell passed the boat was up-ended, nearly throwing Tom and his men out. Fortunately, the next swell lifted the boat again and the Chief Officer threw the fall off the pin of the davit and let go. The boat was pulled away from the ship, then back over the track over which the ship had come. In time they picked up the lifebuoy marker and carried on pulling back. It became time to rest on the oars as it was very hot, with no protection against the sun, while the ship was only a speck on the horizon when it could be seen from the top of the swell.

While lying there a great shark came up alongside, fully the length of the boat which was about fourteen feet. Tom was fascinated watching the small fish swimming over the shark's head. These were striped black and white, horizontally, and acted as pilot fish for the shark.

One of the men took the boat hook and jabbed the big fish in the back. The shark shot off like a torpedo, then came back again at speed and hit the boat head on. They nearly all tipped out, and it was a great wonder that the boat, was not holed. Tom thought it best to keep the boat moving and splash the oars about, but soon he counted seven sharks altogether on each side, much smaller than the first one. Tom knew then that the man they were looking for must be in the insides of those sharks. When sharks taste blood they want more and so become vicious.

Well, now they had to get back to the ship, so Tom tied his shirt on to one of the oars to attract the ship's attention, then they pulled towards her as the ship was now heading in their direction. When close enough he semaphored the situation and asked for life-lines to be given to each man. Every man had a rope on him from the ship in case of any upsetting. All went well, and the boat was hoisted aboard by about ten men on each fall running along the deck. They saw the sharks that had been escorting the boat. He saw the wireless operator standing at the rail and when the ship rolled and brought the deck edge under the water one of the sharks made a leap at his foot, which set him running. No doubt the sharks were hoping there would be a throw-out from the boat. The man that had jumped overboard had suffered from Blackwater fever; they had just picked him up at Port Louis out of the hospital.

The ship was on her way again towards the Suez Canal, and as she came into the Red Sea it was so hot that the firemen were laid out with cramp or a return of the fever. Steam went right back, and the ship was only doing five knots. At one time the engineers were firing the boilers and Tom and the Third Officer were passing the coal into the stokehold. She eventually crawled into Suez and so through the Canal, which was a slow process. On arriving at Port Said fresh bunker coal was taken, this being English and good steaming coal. The ship steamed much better from then on to London.

On reaching the Thames the ship was taken to Greenwich buoys to discharge the sugar for Tate and Lyle's into barges. But the ship did not pay off there, as she was to go to Dartmouth to lay up in the river Dart after the discharging was completed. In due course they tied her up to the buoys in the Dart, just off the town, and she paid off on 21 June 1921. Tom and most of the crew had joined the ship on 6 June 1919 at Hull, so they had been away from the United Kingdom for over two years. In that time the *Arabian Prince* certainly gave everyone plenty to think about.

Tom did not have his sea time in for his Master's examination, having been seventeen months as Third Officer and seven as Second Officer. He needed another five months as a Second Officer to complete his time before going to the examination room.

But the great lay-up of merchant ships was commencing, which made Tom look rather hopelessly into the future.

Fortunately, he had a good pay-off to tide him over until another ship came his way. After a few days at home he entered the Marine School and paid his fees, which would hold good until he gained his Master's certificate. He could not just be idle, nor did life ashore interest him very much. He did not get another ship for three months, but the time at the Marine School was well spent in study, so the days did not hang that heavily.

Conditions were so bad during the slump period that Masters and officers were working at anything they could get, making roads, and doing labouring work in general, and even going to sea in the forecastle on any of the few ships that were moving.

Tom eventually joined the SS *Algerian Prince* late in September 1921 as Second Officer, trading to the Middle East ports and the UK.

Chapter 8

Manchester was the port where he joined the ship. The Captain was a jovial sort, easy to get along with, but the Chief Officer was an elderly man, who had missed his chance of a Master's berth, so he carried a chip on his shoulder. The Third Officer was two years older than Tom, but he only had a Second Mate's certificate. The ship was about four thousand tons deadweight.

This was a very happy period for Tom as life on a home trading ship was very different, as he came back to Manchester or London regularly. The atmosphere was different on board to that of being away for two years. From Manchester the outward voyage would be to Tunis, Malta, Alexandria, Haifa, Beirut, Alexandretta, Mersin and the ports in Cyprus. From London it would be to Malta, Alexandria and Haifa. The British flag was still flying over Palestine, but the Jews were coming in fast by any means they could to beat the quota placed on their entry by the British Government.

Summer-time was the period to load cotton for Manchester, and winter-time was the Jaffa fruit season to any port, to London, Hull or Manchester.

In 1921 Haifa was a very small Arab port, which only boasted a wooden jetty for loading or discharging lighters, and Tom never saw any other ship there at that period. The *Algerian Prince* anchored in a small bay with Mount Carmel towering in the background.

The company's ships were loaded with building material for this port, as it was starting to be built up into a modern city. It was good business for their ships, the London Cement works and reinforcing rod iron from Antwerp. Many of the company's ships were engaged on this trade during the slack period in shipping on other world-wide trades.

Beirut was the main port on the coast, and the company's agents directed the ships from there. Sometimes the *Algerian Prince* lay a few days there, cleaning out and being painted, waiting to go to Jaffa or Cyprus. When going over to Cyprus to load locust beans they took four lighters in tow with about twelve labourers.

These labourers were Turkish Arabs and, like their contemporaries on shore, were fine upright men who had fought alongside the Turks during the war when General Allenby was forcing his way up the coast. The son of the boss stevedore was in charge of the men on the ship, whose job was to stow the locust beans when loading.

The ship would tow the lighters over to Kyrenia, where the beans were seen piled up on the beach in a great heap. The lighters were cast off with a man in each and were towed to the pile by a motor launch. Shore labour filled them up with bulk beans, and these were brought off to the ship, which was lying about half a mile offshore. The gang lifted them aboard in bags, the bags being filled in the lighters, and so the beans were being poured down the hold. When that pile had been loaded, off they would go until another pile was sighted on the beach.

This process went on right around the coast, just picking up the piles of beans where the farmers had dumped them. The Customs official travelled with the ship. Then came Paphos and Zee, which finished the loading, with the lower holds filled with bulk locust beans. The ship then proceeded to Limassol for Customs purposes, also picking up the cargo manifests and bills of lading, together with the clearance, which allowed the ship to leave.

She would then sail on to Beirut to return the lighters and men, afterwards picking up other cargo such as tobacco leaf from Latakia and cotton from Alexandretta and Mersin.

Such a cargo was generally taken to Hull, the locust beans being for cattle food. On some other voyages, after the outward cargo had been discharged on the coast, from Alexandretta sheep and goats would be loaded. These came off in lighters to the ship at anchor. They were loaded in all cargo spaces, filling the lower holds, 'tween decks and weather decks with live sheep and goats. They were hauled on board, about half a dozen in a hoist, by rope around their hind legs.

These would be discharged at Haifa and sometimes at Alexandria. The sheep or goats did not need feeding. These animals when well fed had big tails, which was so when first taken on board, and they could last three days at least without further food or water. Their tails were certainly much smaller when taken to Alexandria as that was about three days' run, whereas to Haifa it was only overnight.

To get anywhere on the ship one had to walk over the backs of the sheep. The goats always managed to stand aloof from the sheep as although they were all mixed up in the loading they were generally found on the forecastle head or poop and even on the boat deck.

Tom never liked that cargo as the ship was in an awful mess when discharged. Holds, 'tween decks and top decks had to be thoroughly washed down, all the dirt removed overboard and all thoroughly sweetened before being allowed in port again to take cargo.

On one particular voyage early in 1921 the ship was bound for Mersin

SS *Algerian Prince.*

in Turkey with a consignment of baled cloth from London. The Greeks and Turks were at a sort of undeclared war with each other. When the ship arrived off the port in the middle watch – Tom's watch as Second Officer – the Captain put the engines at dead slow to make port at 6 a.m. Tom was on the bridge, and the Captain on the next deck below, resting in a deck-chair. It was a very dark night, and with the land so close, Tom saw signalling going on with a morse lamp. He read the message, which was, 'Stop immediately, I am boarding you.' He shouted down to the Captain, who immediately came up and stopped the engines. Out of the darkness a small ship came up and just stood off, sending a boarding party over.

At first Tom thought they were British Naval men as they wore exactly the same uniform, but they turned out to be Greeks. They were armed with rifles, and an officer carried a revolver. They all boarded, and the officer asked to see the manifests, which he scrutinised. Calling the Captain's attention to the bales of cloth, he said they were to be taken off on to his ship, but first the *Algerian Prince* had to follow this other ship to a convenient cove. The *Algerian Prince* anchored and the other ship tied up alongside. This small ship had been a cross-Channel ship, probably Dover to Calais. Now she was a Greek auxiliary cruiser. The lieutenant in charge of these operations was dressed in a uniform similar to a RNR officer in the British Navy.

His men came aboard and transferred the bales to the cruiser. The British men could make no objection with guns at the ready by the armed guards. There must have been about four thousand bales, and being stowed on this deck they were stacked on every available space. The officer, who spoke good English, told Tom about the fighting with the Turks. The bales contained Turkish Army uniforms, which were supposed to be landed at Mersin.

There was something odd about the whole business, as the official who was in charge of dockside operations at Alexandria insisted that the ship should arrive off the port at 3 a.m. which she did. How convenient to find this cruiser waiting for the ship. The official was a Greek himself.

When the bales were taken out, the ship went into Mersin with only two cases of cotton goods. A Turkish Army officer came off to the ship, and when he saw the bales were gone he naturally became very angry, and immediately went back on shore with the threat to arrest the Captain. As there were only two cases to discharge, the Chief Officer had them slung and hanging overboard ready to drop into a lighter.

The anchor chain was hove in until the anchor was just resting on the bottom, and the engines put at stand-by. A lighter full of soldiers was approaching the ship, and when it came alongside the two cases were dropped among the soldiers, causing some confusion. The anchor was tripped, the engines put at full speed and so the ship left port.

Arriving back in Alexandria, it was heard that questions had been asked in Parliament about this incident, but Tom did not hear any more about the affair. Shortly afterwards the Turks invaded a Turkish town, Smyrna, which was full of Greeks, massacred a great number and others fled in ships as fast as they could, which ended the state of hostilities.

When the citrus fruit season came round, from October to April, the ship would load cases of oranges at Jaffa, where she would lie about half a mile off the port. The weather had to be good when lying so close inshore, and being winter-time strong winds would blow down the coast from the north. The ship then had to heave up and just stand off until the weather decided to change for the better.

Lighters full of oranges in boxes would swarm around the ship. They would be quickly emptied and go back for more. Being stowed down the holds, leaving space for ventilation, and given fine weather the ship would soon be loaded, even having oranges on deck as well. Tel Aviv at that time was just a barren headland opposite Jaffa.

Tom did four voyages on this ship in just over twelve months, so he had his sea time in for his Master's certificate. He left the ship and went back to the Marine School at South Shields, and soon he was studying for this certificate.

After three months of intensive study he decided to present himself before the examiner at South Shields. Fortunately, he passed first time and, according to the examiner, gained marks of 97 per cent. Well, that was that. Now he had all the necessary qualifications to work his way up to be Master of a steamship. He was only lacking in experience. The examiner suggested that he should have a go at Extra Master, but shipping being in a poor way at the time, Tom thought he would carry on studying at the Marine School. The instructors were excellent men and knew their job. In the meantime he informed the Prince Line that he had gained his Master's certificate. The date stamped on his certificate was 2 December 1922. He got nicely settled at school again and felt in the mood to tackle the work for this extra certificate. Unfortunately, he was offered a Second Officer's berth on another ship sailing from Manchester on Christmas Eve. Tom thought hard about accepting that berth, but his money was low and the only way to earn more was to go back to sea, so he accepted.

The ship, SS *Cyprian Prince*, was on the same trade as the *Algerian Prince*. After two voyages she laid up in Manchester, everyone being paid off, so Tom went home and back to school.

Chapter 9

THIS TIME TOM WAS BACK at the school for about five months. He was in a big room on his own, which was also the room the chaps who were up for a Second Mate's certificate came into to study chartwork, and in time he found he was teaching them this chartwork.

He did his best to master the extra subjects, which included making charts from the surveyors' information, also such subjects as engines and boilers. General science was something else of which he had to have a good knowledge. Nevertheless, without any lectures on the subjects he had to endeavour to master the textbooks where a friendly word here and there would have often cleared up some problem.

Owing to the slump in shipping Tom found the school was full of students at a loose end, who would otherwise have been away at sea. No other jobs were open to them unless they had some certificate indicating their degree of intelligence, and the few lecturers were hard pushed to attend to such students.

Tom in the meantime had found a girl friend. Being a lonely chap when ashore, he liked her company.

The time came when he decided to go up for the examination. He was the only Extra Master, against the numerous First and Second Mates. The examiners, being human, allowed Tom a little extra time after hours. When he came to be examined reading morse and semaphore signals, the examiner grabbed a passing youth, who was just going out of the door, to mark for him, and Tom had to deal with this chap moaning about losing his train while he was trying to read signals which were being sent out at twice the speed of an ordinary certificate requirement.

Up until Friday of the exam week Tom thought he had not done so badly, when in walked the Chief Examiner from London to have a look around. He immediately decided to take over Tom, to ease his colleagues of some of the massive paper work they had to go through.

First he called Tom up to his desk and told him he would have marks of 84 per cent which he considered was not enough. He did not say what was enough. He asked a question on general science, but Tom did not answer as he had no idea of the object mentioned although it was simple enough, as he later found on looking up his book. The examiner gave Tom a searching look then told him to come back next week, so Tom took the hint and left.

Thinking he had to go through the whole of the examination again, he felt he could not do it to his credit, so he went to the Mercantile Marine Superintendent for his papers, which included his Master's certificate, with a view to looking for a ship. Strange to say, the Superintendent tried to persuade Tom to have another go at the examination, for, as he remarked, he would be sure to pass. Tom nevertheless decided to look for a job, as he had no money left and did not want to be a burden on his family as conditions were tough.

The Prince Line could not offer him anything so, being a member of the Merchant Officers Guild, he decided to give them a call at South Shields, where he was examined. The Guild's office was in the old town hall in the centre of the market place, being a building of ancient origin, not far from the river Tyne. Without any further hesitation he repaired there to ask if any jobs were going. Tom must have been optimistic, as the river was full of laid-up ships.

He saw the Guild representative, who was an ex–Master, and, strangely enough, a Second Mate's job had suddenly turned up, on a ship lying in Sunderland Docks. Tom immediately went down to investigate. The ship was the *Glenmore* of Glasgow and was busy taking bunker coal. Tom had a word with the Chief Officer, the Captain not being on board. The ship was about eight thousand tons deadweight and of ancient origin, going out to Cuba to load sugar for the UK. She only carried two officers beside the Captain, namely the Chief and the Second, who were on watches four hours on and four off.

Tom was told that he would find the Captain at a certain pub in South Shields, where he had gone with the Superintendent. Tom soon found the pub, so went in to find these two gentlemen. They were easy to contact as they were at the bar counter. The Captain was a fairly young man, and the Super was a well set-up gentleman from Glasgow. He belonged to a firm of surveyors who attended to ships of owners who had no superintendents of their own for the period they were in port. Tom was told that the previous Second Mate, who had an Extra Master's certificate, had been sent to hospital with German measles, by the port doctor.

Tom gave them his particulars and asked if he could have the job as Second Mate. He also mentioned his attempt for the Extra Master's certificate. He was readily given the berth, so he collected a few odds and ends and proceeded to join the *Glenmore*, also informing the Prince Line of his whereabouts.

The ship was to sail next day, so Tom signed the agreement at wages of about thirteen pounds per month. Next day, however, the port doctor came on board and informed the Captain that the old Second Mate had to have his berth back, as it was found that he did not have German measles after all. The Captain and Super were on board and Tom was called up to see them. They were very concerned about having to sign Tom off again, but the Super promised him the very first berth which became vacant, as they had a new ship nearly ready.

Just then who should come on board but Tom's young sister, who had taken an afternoon off school at their mother's direction because a telegram had arrived that morning from the Prince Line for Tom and she was making sure it was delivered. When Tom opened the telegram it said, 'Offer the *Algerian Prince* in a fortnight's time as Second Officer.'

Everybody was very pleased that things had been settled amicably and Tom's little sister was taken over by the Captain's wife until Tom picked up his odds and ends, then off they went home in high spirits.

Sure enough, Tom was soon back in his old ship again, with the meals coming in regularly. Tom's wages were twenty pounds per month on the *Algerian Prince*, so he and his girl friend decided to be married in the near future.

On the second voyage the Chief Officer was put into hospital at Malta with a bad dose of influenza, so Tom was temporarily promoted to Chief Officer until the ship arrived at Alexandria, as the company had another man in view on one of the company's ships there. It was promotion for the other fellow, so that was that.

Tom had decided to be married at the end of this very voyage, so when the ship arrived at Manchester with a cargo of citrus fruit from Jaffa he made arrangements to have fourteen days' leave, which would be the period the ship was in port before commencing to load outwards. The Superintendent in Manchester had made those arrangements for him, and as he was going down the gangway to go home the Super came up with instructions from the owners to the effect that Tom had to leave the *Algerian Prince* and proceed to join the *Siberian Prince* in the dry dock at South Shields. This was Saturday, and he had to join on the Monday morning. He was going to be married on the Tuesday, and all arrangements had been made. Tom was told to fix up his domestic affairs with the Captain of the *Siberian Prince*.

Chapter 10

Tom had no intention of putting himself out of employment again; in fact, he was wondering why he was in such a hurry to get married. The ship he was to join was going to the River Plate and back to the UK. The company were sending him to this ship to gain further experience with a view to promotion in the near future.

It was with mixed feelings that he joined the ship on the Monday after a weekend at home, having explained matters to his understanding fiancée. He found the ship would be in the dry dock until the following Saturday, which put another outlook on domestic matters, so he asked the Captain if he could be absent the next day to be married. Consent was readily given, and he was to be on board on Wednesday. That was good enough for Tom, and he was married on Tuesday, 12 February 1924, his wife's twenty-third birthday, Tom being two years older.

There was plenty of work to be done on the *Siberian Prince*. She was taking bunker coal while in the dry dock, with barges being outside the dock gates and using dockyard cranes. She was going out in ballast. The charts had to be attended to, and a batch of new ones had to be tallied and checked, together with other stores.

The Chief Officer needed some help to check his stores. The crew had to be signed on, which meant much shipping office work for Tom. His wife would come aboard in the afternoon and sometimes he had a night at home, and so it all went on until the ship left for the River Plate.

She went up-river as far as San Nicolas to commence loading, just below Rosario. The ship was moored to a high cliffside and buoys. Chutes were rigged from the warehouses on top of the cliff to the ship's holds. Bags of maize came down the chutes on to the hatch top where they were received and opened, the grain being poured into the hold in bulk. The loading was very quick by this method, and in a few days the ship was down to twenty-one feet draft fore and aft, being the draft required to cross the bar at Martin Garcia, where the deeper waters of the River Plate were met. About four thousand tons of bulk grain were loaded here.

On reaching the bar the ship had to anchor and a watch kept on tide gauges ashore, which indicated the depth of water over the bar. When the indications showed the water was rising the ship was made ready to move across as soon as the water had risen to its highest at about twenty-three feet, then she would go over at full speed, making for Buenos Aires, where the loading was completed and the bulk secured on top by stowing bags of grain all over the bulk.

Tom had not been to Buenos Aires since his apprentice days. He met Canon Brady again, and visited the Seamen's Mission, where the usual recreations were indulged in. He had not any money to spare, being married now and preparing to set up a home.

When Tom was promoted to Second Officer all their wages were reduced, so that he still received the same amount as he did when he was Third Officer. Strange to say the same happened when he was promoted to Chief Officer, and he still carried the same wages of £20 per month until he was promoted to Master on 1 May 1939, when he received £32 per month. Of course Tom was fortunate to be in more or less continuous employment during the slump period between the wars.

After completing loading, his ship sailed for the United Kingdom. The port of discharge was never disclosed until in home waters, as buying and selling of the cargo went on at the grain market before the port was decided for discharging purposes.

Orders were received by radio, and this time the cargo was to be discharged at Rank's Mill in Victoria Docks, London. When she arrived there Tom's job was finishing off the accounts for the wages for all on board, so it was generally far into the night before things were ready for paying off. Next morning one of the clerks brought the cash down to the ship after being informed of the exact amount. Pay envelopes were made out, and all the crew would appear before the Mercantile Marine Superintendent at the nearest shipping office. When all had received their due the Second Officer had the job of making out the Captain's Portage Account with the owners.

Chapter 11

TOM FOUND THAT BEING MARRIED did not fit in with his present employment, if he wanted to carry on and remain in the company. Conditions however were so bad ashore and in shipping that he was fortunate to have employment at all.

His wife came down to London, and he had her installed in comfortable lodgings. They were happy together, and when Tom had any liberty they would pop up to the city and see the sights, including the 1924 Exhibition which was in full swing at Wembley.

When discharging was completed at London, the ship proceeded to the river Tyne for bunkers and Tom was allowed to take his wife home on the ship.

From the Tyne the *Siberian Prince* was taken around to Liverpool. She then went on to the company's North Atlantic trade, with voyages of about one month from Liverpool to Boston. Between the Christmas and New Year the company decided to ship a full Chinese crew, so far as the ratings were concerned. These men were not allowed on board until the cargo was loaded, this being the Stevedores' Union rules. When the cargo was loaded and the crew were on board the ship sailed for Boston, USA, with no time to shake the crew down.

The Chinese were from a boarding house in Rotterdam, and they must have been all the undesirables to be shipped out of the country. They were a mixture of Hong Kong and Shanghai men, which is a bad mixture to start with, as the two are different types altogether.

On arrival in Boston, the snow was thick everywhere. After a few days the cargo was discharged, and the *Siberian Prince* was ordered to New York to go on the Far East berth. Tom had a very pleasant surprise when the Captain handed him a telegram one day, which informed him that he was the father of a fine big son and that all was well. The news got around, so Tom had to do the honours as a proud father. Little did he know the extent of time that would pass before he could see his son. At the time of the birth there was, while in Boston, a total eclipse of the sun by the moon, which was viewed by all on board.

While in New York the Chinese crew were not allowed on shore leave, or even to leave the ship at all. Special watchmen were stationed on the ship and ashore to see that none did leave. But the Chinese Bandary cook for the crew had other ideas, as he would slip down a rope over the side into one of the lighters and jump from one lighter to another towards the shore. He would be heading for Chinatown in New York, but he was always caught not far from the ship. His dress alone gave him away, besides his lost look. Some said he was a little off balance, and Tom thought it could be a case of instability after cooking for over thirty men.

The ship loaded case oil for the lamps of China, together with a certain amount of general cargo. When completed at that port Tom was having the final look at the draft, which had to be recorded on certain documents for Head Office, when he noticed the rudder was not amidships but at an angle. Going on to the bridge he hoped to put it right by a turn of the wheel, but up there it was dead on the centre. Going aft he saw the quadrant too was on the centre line and looking over the stern he saw the rudder was not.

He reported this to the Chief Officer, and the Lloyd's surveyor and the Superintendent had a close-up look at the rudder post from staging and found it was cracked.

The ship had to go into dry dock for three days while the rudder post was repaired. Tom remarked it was just as well he found something wrong then as it is a long way from Panama to Japan. The voyage proceeded after things were put right again, calling at Newport News for loading hogsheads of tobacco leaf and other products of the weed. Coal bunkers were also taken for the long voyage, and so the *Siberian Prince* left Newport News for the Panama Canal, which was new to Tom.

The Captain had been a prisoner of war in Austria for two years during the Great War, and it was he who had taken over the *Merchant Prince* when Tom was Third Officer. He had some interesting theories on winds and tides and other subjects. They generally came out at the meal table, so that it was quite a pleasure to sit down to a meal and discuss the various topics. The Captain was always at the head of the table with the Chief Officer on one side of him and the Chief Engineer on the other, the Second Officer being next to his Chief and Third Officer next to the Second. The engineers had their mess room, and so did the apprentices.

All officers had to be properly dressed in uniform, and no half measures were entertained. When the weather became too warm the Captain issued orders to wear white uniforms. Off watch there was no harm in making oneself comfortable, to preserve the cleanliness of the uniforms, but short-sleeved shirts and white shorts were never heard of in those days.

In port, for climbing up and down holds white boiler suits were the thing. On the River Plate trade each officer had plenty of hard work to do, such as preparing holds for cargo and putting up shifting boards, as mostly, when on grain charters, no time had to be wasted between charters.

The *Siberian Prince* was only an eleven-knot ship under the best of conditions, so it took them about ten days to reach the Atlantic side of the Panama Canal.

The Canal had only been opened to shipping in 1914, and Tom remembered as a small boy being interested in pictures of the building of it seen in magazines.

It was quite an experience to see the ship lifted up through the various locks at Gatun into Gatun Lake, which is an artificial lake, being a flooded valley with tops of trees still to be seen then above the water level. After winding through the Rock Cut and then lowered by two stages in Miraflores locks, they went two miles further on to the San Miguel Lock, which lowered the ship one stage to the level of the Pacific Ocean. A United States pilot took over for the transit through, as at each lock six electric locomotives, three on each side, held the ship when the locks were filling with water or vice versa.

They were in a new ocean for Tom, which to him was very thrilling. When clear of the Panama Gulf, the course was set on the great circle for Honolulu where coal bunkers would be taken and then to Yokohama in Japan. This was a fine weather voyage, so Tom had plenty of time to correct the charts and do other jobs in his line. His watch on the bridge was twelve to four in the afternoon and the same hours in the morning. After coming off watch at 4 a.m. he would usually join his opposite number from the engine room, the Third Engineer, over a cup of tea and yarn about nothing in particular. There were no radios in those days to enliven the passing hours. Chronometers had to be wound at 8 a.m. each day, and the daily rate applied to the error. They were checked by time ball at Honolulu.

After a passage of thirty-five days, the ship arrived at Yokohama, then on to Kobe and so to Karatsu for coal bunkers. Passing through the Inland Sea out through the Shimonseki Channel on the north-west of the sea, the First Mate and Tom were having tea when they heard the Captain shouting, 'Let go the anchor!'

Tom looked out of the porthole to see what was happening and gazed right into the faces of some Japanese fishermen standing on the edge of the shore. They were so close that it seemed the ship would soon be ashore. He shot out of that saloon like a jack-rabbit on to the bridge and saw that the Chinese quartermaster had, with the Captain as excited as anything, temporarily lost control of the steering. Tom took over the steering and, following the Japanese pilot's orders, eased the ship away from the shore into mid-channel, and so carried on until the ship was clear of all danger. The strong tide running the opposite way to the ship's course had caught her fair on a turning movement, which had forced the ship close to the shore, and in the confusion of raised voices the helmsman had aided the ship on her way to possible disaster by not being quick enough at answering the helm as required.

The *Siberian Prince* soon arrived at Karatsu after that event, anchoring off the port, and bunkering commenced. The ship was bunkered by women standing on wooden stages over the ship's side, passing small baskets of coal up to other groups higher up and tipping down into the bunker space. A constant stream was maintained on both sides from barges by a countless number of small Japanese women.

After taking bunker coal the ship proceeded to Shanghai. Manual labour at this port seemed to be plentiful, and the ship was swarming with coolies in no time. A British pilot took the ship up the Woo Sung River. There were hundreds of junks on the water coming and going, through which the ship practically pushed her way. Excitable Chinese families on the junks appeared to dislike the ship pushing through and the jabber and noise was terrific. Eventually the ship docked at a riverside godown, and work was started to unload heavy cases of machinery. A large ten-ton case, after it landed on the wharf, was surrounded by as many coolies as possible.

The case was lifted and moved at a slow march, by manual efforts only, to the godown. Each two men had a piece of hard wood across their shoulders with a short length of rope on either end attached to a hook. The hooks were placed under the bottom of the case, and with this swarm of couples around the case, number one man gave the signal and all lifted at the same time, and walked away with the case to the godown. Labour was so cheap that a contractor was hired to paint the ship round, and they finished the job in one day, painting the hull and the boot-topping red and all the white paintwork on the deck houses.

The ship only stopped there one day and then sailed to Hong Kong. There all the Chinese that had been shipped at Liverpool were laid off and a new crew engaged, which was easy enough. Tom was ashore with the Captain, engaged on this project. The Serangs were picked first, then they brought along their own men.

The Chief Officer had no more bother with his crew after that. They were fine men, British subjects, and the Serangs had full control of them. The same applied to the other departments, and life was much easier now. The ship lay in Hong Kong for two or three days before sailing to Manila in the Philippines.

Tom was fascinated with Hong Kong. It was a city of great attraction to him and his friends aboard ship. At night it looked like fairyland when viewed from the ship, with all the lights on the mountain side of Victoria.

The wireless operator and Tom had the occasional night ashore so they would wander around the native quarters and watch the people working. All was in full swing at ten o'clock at night and no doubt into the early hours of the morning. The blacksmiths, silversmiths, tailors and every handicraft trade imaginable, were all out in the open. All this industry would be embellished with tapping of two hardwood sticks and the sound of Chinese men and women passing to and fro in wooden sandals; sandwiched between the hives of industry were the cook shops with open fronts, dishing out all kinds of queer concoctions to all and sundry for the matter of a coin or two. It surely was a sight which Tom and his friend found most astonishing and interesting. Great kerosene flares lit up the whole area.

The ship discharged all the case oil at this port, over at the Kowloon side. It was slung up out of the hold, so many boxes in a rope sling, and landed on the wharf where numerous Chinese women waited, each with a wooden piece across her shoulders, with two rope slings at each end.

They would slip each sling over a case and so shuffle along, balancing the cases across their shoulders for some considerable distance to the depot. This was all kerosene for lamps, as at that time electricity played no part in their lighting system.

As this discharging berth was some distance away, it was quite a walk into town, although there were plenty of rickshaws to take one. Tom and the Third Engineer liked a walk to stretch their legs, and walking along this road one night they came across a dead Chinese woman. They could only report the matter to the police when they met any, but merely to look at the body filled Tom and his friend with great sympathy for Chinese women, as this one must have collapsed with sheer weariness after a hard day's work. She was not very old by the look of her. What a life it was for women in China.

After the case oil had been discharged all the holds were cleaned out ready for loading cargo, in Manila, where the deep tanks were filled and cleaned using local labour to get rid of the rust and polish all the steelwork to carry coconut oil. After the surveyor arranged the heating coils and saw them tested the tank was also tested for tightness, then filled with about five hundred tons of bulk coconut oil.

She also loaded bags of sugar and hemp, then sailed for Surabaya in Java, where cases of rubber were loaded. The ship had to be thoroughly measured in the matter of empty space in the holds, and the information gained had to be passed on to the next port, Batavia, so they could judge what spaces they wanted for their cargo.

On arrival at Batavia, the capital of Java, Tom was well occupied looking after the stowage of the cargo. As long as cargo was being loaded all the officers were on duty, seeing that it was properly stowed and dunnaged.

After it was loaded the measuring up had to be done for Singapore. On arrival there the official measurers came on board and measured all the spaces. It was a very important business as the cargo was booked all the way up the coast to Penang, guaranteeing the shipping of all cargo booked. Later ships were lucky if they got any cargo at all out there.

Space had to be left for loading tea at Colombo in the 'tween decks, so Tom had his hands full, together with quite a deal of clerical work such as cargo plans and giving cash out to the crew under the instructions of the Captain. The Chief Officer had full charge of the loading, and was responsible for keeping the ship clean and painted and his cargo gear in first-class condition.

Tom was very interested in all the ports he visited, and if the opportunity offered he liked to ramble round and see how people lived. There were many places in Singapore worth seeing such as the Botanical Gardens, a cricket match now and again, a pop in to the Seamen's Mission to have a yarn with the padre, or a sit on the verandah of a decent hotel with a large glass of lager close at hand.

Loading a ship of the *Siberian Prince* type was a very difficult job, as she was a general purpose ship — in other words a tramp. Many delicate cargoes were loaded out East which required special stowage. Spices and essential oils were cargoes that could contaminate each other if stowed in the same compartment. Rubber was usually stowed or packed in tea chests, being easy to stow as long as the cases had no breakages on account of an uneven stow. Chips of wood from a broken case could pierce several of the outer sheets of rubber inside the case and cause considerable damage.

After calling at Penang and finishing loading on the coast, the ship proceeded to Colombo. Ships were tied up to buoys at that port and the cargo was loaded from barges. Cases of tea had to be stowed in upper spaces, and each shipper of cases of tea had his own special mark to identify them. Those marks had to be stowed together, so that they could easily be found at the discharging port. Often the consignee asked for their chests to be discharged as early as possible, which could easily be done when they were stowed in one block.

Other cargoes picked up at Colombo were chests of desiccated coconut and bags of pepper, but tea was the most abundant. Colombo offered many attractions for tourists, but rarely did Tom or his fellow officers get any opportunity to go ashore. As it was the last port of loading, work carried on day and night until completed. Tom and the Third Officer had to see to the stowage and then to the seaworthy certificates and the documents required by Head Office in the United Kingdom and ports of discharge in the United States.

When all was completed the ship sailed for Boston and New York via the Suez Canal. If sailing between May and September the south-west monsoon was blowing, which is the bad weather monsoon in the Arabian Sea. A ten or eleven-knot ship made a long passage to avoid the heavy westerly gales and high seas by keeping well south on the 7½ degrees latitude north, and when reaching fifty degrees east made up for Cape Guardafui at the north-east corner of Africa, being helped along then by a current running up the African coast.

Once into the Gulf of Aden it was smooth water all the way. Between October and April fine weather prevails and a direct route could be made to Guardafui.

The *Siberian Prince* then proceeded through the Gulf of Aden, passing Perim Island, into the Red Sea then into the Gulf of Suez and so to the southern end of the Suez Canal at Port Tufic. A canal pilot boarded there to take the ship through the canal to Port Said where more bunker coal was taken.

Arriving at Port Said always gave Tom the feeling of leaving the romantic and mysterious part of the world behind, like coming out of Aladdin's cave in the story books, to everyday familiar surroundings.

The ship would soon be on her way through the Mediterranean, passing Gibraltar in due course, then across the Atlantic to Boston. At that port the Captain would enter the ship as the first port of arrival. Stevedores would board and soon part of the Far Eastern cargo would be on the wharf, ready for delivery to the consignees.

From there she would proceed to New York, taking the outward passage via Cape Cod, keeping a good way off the land and then making for Nantucket Lightship. Rounding this, a straight course would take her to the Ambrose Lightship at the entrance to New York Bay. There the pilot would board and take the ship to the company's pier, where two or three tugs would take over with one of the tug captains on the bridge giving signals on a pea whistle as to whether he wanted the tugs to push or pull.

The *Siberian Prince* was now docked, and the stevedores came on board and unloaded the cargo as fast as they could. In a day or so the covered-in wharf where the cargo was landed began to smell like Singapore with the different cargoes from there and the other ports.

Those were exciting days for Tom. He was of a romantic turn of mind, for what man of the sea is not? No one got bored if he loved the life. It was an education in itself to meet the people of other nations and be able to call some of them your personal friends.

So here was Tom, after eleven years following the sea. He had done his job to the best of his ability, had a life full of activity, possessed a Master Mariner's Certificate and was very self-reliant, though perhaps simple in his outlook as the world's problems did not bother him. The books he liked to read were from the pen of Charles Dickens, and he found great pleasure in the style and period of those works.

He also had a good wife, and a son he had not yet seen. The anticipation of doing so in the near future he relished in secret,

Changes were happening on the *Siberian Prince* in New York, one of which was that Tom was promoted to Chief Officer of the *African Prince*.

Chapter 12

THE *African Prince* was lying on the other side of the dock, having discharged a cargo of coffee from Brazil. The Chief Officer was going home after two years on the Brazilian trade.

Tom was twenty-six years old now and probably looked young, but he had the experience and qualifications. He duly reported to the Captain of the *African Prince* and saw the Chief Officer who was leaving who put him wise to everything he should know about the ship. The Chief Officer eventually sailed for home in a Cunard passenger ship.

Tom was signed on and he was now Number One officer. The ship was about eight thousand tons deadweight and a very sturdy one, being exceptionally strongly built. The Captain was a man of forty-five years of age, and Tom was warned that he was difficult to get along with, but he took all that in his stride. The Second Officer was ten years older than himself, and had spent the war years in the Navy as Lieutenant RNR on mine-sweeping trawlers. He had only just joined the company. The Third Officer was a young man with a Second Mate's certificate, and he had had an excellent education at Westminster. The Chief Engineer was an old Scot from Edinburgh.

Tom took the ship's position night and morning by stars, all ready for his worship's approval, so he beat the old man to it although he was only twenty-six years of age. The cargo itself was a whole time job in port, all the officers tallying and Tom's gang down in the hold draping all the steel work with separation cloths for loading coffee beans in bags. The Chief Engineer was near to retirement age – a big stout Scotsman. The old man hated him, but Tom found him to be a jolly good friend, and while Tom was ashore with him Tom was in good hands. No throwing money away with that old boy. One time in New Orleans they had been up the road for a feed of ham and eggs and on walking back the Chief Engineer suddenly disappeared off the edge of the path. There was a deep gully down the side of the path to carry away excess water after heavy rains. This gully was covered over with steel covers on hinges to protect the people who might walk off the path. One happened to be open, and down the Chief went up to his neck. It was some job to get him out, but they managed. Tom thought the whole incident very amusing, but not the Chief. He was a big man to go falling down holes in the road, but it happened so quickly and without a sound, he was there one minute, and gone the next. To give an idea of the Chief, he was like J.T. Sullivan the boxer; in fact some wag had put a picture of the boxer in the mess room to emphasise the similarity.

The Bosun was a Swede and the sailors were of all nationalities. Tom now had to take control of these men and run the ship to the best of his ability.

The Second Officer did his work without much ado, but Tom could not call him friendly by any means. The Third Officer was a good lad, but Tom wondered why he had taken up a sea career. Strange things were happening to all people during the awful depression in England and in the world generally.

For the first voyage Tom was finding his way about. The ship loaded at the dock and sailed for Santos in Brazil. During the loading the Chief Officer had to plan out the cargo loading and, in conjunction with the head stevedore, map out the stowage.

The voyage from New York to Santos was a fine weather voyage. The speed of the ship was about ten knots with the ordinary triple expansion steam engine, burning about thirty-five tons of coal per day to maintain that speed.

The Captain gave Tom a few hints about how he expected the ship to be smart and clean on arriving at any port, with awnings to be scrubbed clean and stretched taut on all occasions, and the wooden decks, which were teakwood, to be holystoned every Saturday. All cargo gear was to be taken down, overhauled and stowed away, out of the weather, which Tom thought a good idea. The wooden derricks had to be cleaned to the bare wood and well coated with raw linseed oil. The wooden topmasts, too, had to have this treatment.

A canvas mast coat had to be lashed on the main topmast so that it could not deteriorate under the influence of smoke from the funnel. Well, that was something to go on. It was no use falling foul of the Captain during his first voyage as Chief Officer by trying to exercise other ideas. Not that there was anything wrong with the Captain's ideas. The steel decks, not being wooden sheathed, had to be scaled clean and coated with a concoction of crude oil, black paint and dryers. This ship had had her hull built before the war, and when war came she was apparently left on the stocks and not launched until 1917 when she was completed. Her hull had much thicker plating than a post-war ship and was more durable.

Tom saw to it that the Captain's suggestions were carried out, and duly received credit for same. Tom thought, too, that a well-kept ship, of clean appearance, gave everyone who sailed in her a sense of pride which went a long way to maintaining discipline. The crew's quarters were painted up

SS *African Prince* 1927.

and all put in good order once a voyage, which made men who were inclined to mess the place up think twice and change their ideas.

Tom found he was getting on well with the Captain, as he often entrusted him with his confidence, and he found out that he was buying the ship chandlers' business at Santos. This was verified the next voyage, which was the Captain's last before he 'swallowed the anchor'.

Although Tom was promoted his pay did not increase. The National Maritime Board, which consisted of representatives of shipowners and officers and engineers, had decided to reduce the wages of all. So by being promoted Tom retained the same remuneration he had been receiving as Second Officer. This had happened at the time he was promoted to Second Officer. From Third Officer until his promotion his wages were the same, at twenty pounds per month, which gave no reward at all for his extra responsibility.

Tom could see good cargoes were being carried on the American coast, from north to south and back again, and the reductions did not tune in with his way of thinking, especially when officers were expected to do two years away from home. The sailors and firemen were signing on at New York on United States wages, as the crews were changed each voyage. They were not affected, although US wages were about the same as for home seamen, but in dollars. The axe held over the officers and engineers was unemployment, which was rife all over the world, as well as at home. Also, no dole or unemployment pay was paid to officers, as they were excluded from paying into the National Insurance under the pretence of not being manual workers.

So Tom put it out of his mind, and hoped the situation would be straightened out some day. There was not even any sort of pension scheme before 1938.

When the Captain of the *African Prince* left the ship at New York, who should join but the last Chief Officer as Captain. Tom was pleased, as he appeared a pleasant chap to sail with. By now Tom was fully competent to carry on, as he knew the ship from keel to truck.

They sailed again for Santos as a great number of boxed Ford cars were going out to Brazil, of the Model 'T' type. When they were discharged at Santos, the casings would be taken off on the dockside. They would then be set up in running order and pushed off under their own steam, so to speak.

Santos had been an infected port when Tom first sailed into it. Now it was a health resort, as all the improvements were completed which had been going on during the war. Tom remembered the shiploads of sewage pipes which had been lying about during his early days when the work was just starting.

Gonzaga was the seaside resort, which had developed on the coast only a short car ride from the centre of Santos, and the Chief Engineer and Tom liked to go there in the evenings. Just outside the town was another place of interest called the 'Mirama', a large casino where roulette and all kinds of other gambling were going on. The Chief and Tom were not interested in the gambling, but in the grounds was an open-air cinema, which was free viewing if you sat at the table with a glass of beer at hand, and a pleasant evening could be spent there for next to nothing. People of consequence would visit the gambling tables and spend a lot of money, which paid for the additional entertainment.

Tom had heard of some officers winning a packet one night and losing it the next, but Tom and the Chief had not that kind of money to throw away.

On the voyage when the new Captain took over, the ship received orders to go to Buenos Aires to load a full cargo of grain on charter for home, and all on board were very happy at the news. From Santos she sailed to the River Plate, loaded up and made for home. It could be anywhere in the home trade limits, the Continent or UK ports, but the final orders were for London.

On arriving there the ship went to Victoria Docks, and the cargo was discharged into barges. Tom was delighted to have his wife and baby son to join him there as he did not intend to leave the ship because Lord knows when he would have been employed again.

Unfortunately, a coal strike was on at home, and the owners wanted the ship away as soon as possible, so she was discharged in less than a week, going over to Rotterdam for bunker coal, which meant he did not have long with his wife and child. They were however getting a tidy little home together and looked forward to buying a new house. Tom was delighted to see his son, after being away from home for one and a half years, which was also the age of his son.

The ship went direct to New York, and changed the crew there. It was now March 1926.

Chapter 13

T HE *African Prince* loaded in the 'tween decks cargo for Santos on this voyage, for general cargo, and then went to Newport News and filled the lower holds with a coal cargo for the Argentine Railways, to be discharged at Buenos Aires. While in Santos the Chief Engineer and Tom were sitting in a cosy bar, having a glass of beer, when the manager came over with the local paper and translated to them news about the General Strike in the UK. It all sounded very alarming and had the appearance of a revolution.

The crew of the *African Prince* were all Brazilians, however, except for the officers and engineers, so there was not much to worry about there. On arrival at Buenos Aires, where English language newspapers were printed, Tom got the whole story, and it seemed that everything was under control.

When the cargo was discharged the ship was washed down in the holds and all over, as the river water was pure fresh water. This was done while steaming up to the loading port at Rosario. When loaded down to twenty-one feet draft they came back to Buenos Aires to finish off loading.

This cargo was discharged at Ipswich, anchoring off Pin Mill, as the ship could not go up the river as far as the town docks. The same type of voyage occupied the *African Prince* again, but returning to Bremen this time. The Brazilian crew were sent back to New York as the crew of another company's steamer, which was lying at Calais. Tom had the job of taking those men by train to Calais, and after many difficulties they all eventually arrived at the French port, having taken the best part of two days and one night. Tom found the attendants very helpful on each train he travelled. They had to change trains at Aachen, Brussels and Lille, and it must have been quite a scene watching thirty men dashing for their connections. One of the attendants would accompany Tom in the wild dash to the train, taking them further on over bridges and platforms, and finally squeezing the whole lot into various carriages where room could be found amongst fat old ladies and, in many cases, crates of fowls whose owners had been to the market. The squawking of these fowls added to the confusion.

Arriving in Brussels at 5 a.m. it was a problem to find breakfast for all of them. They had an hour to wait for the next train, so Tom made one of the Brazilian stewards interpreter and they marched out of the station at Brussels, as no buffet was open there.

They had to go some way before finding a café open, then, coming across one with the door open and a girl scrubbing the floor, they walked in and sat at the tables. The girl was shouting 'Fadder', and an elderly man popped his head around the door. Tom's interpreter went to work on him to order thirty plates of bacon and eggs, explaining who they were, and Tom showed him his money to put the old man at ease.

Soon he had the whole family up and the breakfast in the making. It was served with plenty of coffee and real old French rolls, and the gang tucked in. Tom paid him what he asked for in the correct currency, as he had been given sufficient money in three currencies, German, Belgian and French.

When all were satisfied, Tom marched them back to the station and boarded the train, having to push them in anywhere. They were happy, though, and whenever he could get food of some description, and coffee when on the train or when it stopped at other stations, he did so.

Working on this system they stopped at one big station, and Tom saw a man pushing a coffee and sandwich barrow on the platform. He served them all, and just as Tom was paying the vendor of the goods out on the platform he saw the train moving out. He threw some money to the man

Four apprentices of SS *African Prince* 1929.

and made a dash for the moving train. He just caught it and was pulled into the carriage by the train attendant.

Crossing the various countries' borders was another exciting time, as Tom had all the men's passports, etc. and so had to deal with Customs officers and immigration officials but the steward who was helping Tom with the language got over any bother, and Tom found it all very exciting and full of fun.

On this journey Tom was pleased to find how helpful everyone was with whom he came into contact, which meant the ordinary man or woman who might be sharing the railway carriage or met in the street. At one station, changing trains meant going from one side of the town to the other. Thirty men made quite a crowd when inquiring the directions, but they got by with many a cheery wave of the hand.

Tom had a marvellous journey back to Bremen, just taking his time. At Lille, instead of dashing for the other train, he stopped off and had a look around the near neighbourhood, taking his seat at a table outside a café, and enjoying a little food and drink. After an hour or so of this leisure, strolling back to the station, he found the train to Brussels was leaving at 6 a.m. He explained to the station-master that he was travelling on that train, first-class, so he very kindly had the carriage door unlocked in order that Tom could sleep there, with toilet and wash-basin handy.

He was three days and two nights returning to the ship. Next he was given three weeks' leave at home, and arranged with the German ship chandler to fix him up with a passage on a coaster going over to Hull. It was a German coaster, and another youngish man was also taking passage to Hull. They got on friendly terms and Tom found he was associating with the son of the Mayor of Bremen. When Tom left the ship at Hull he had a pressing invitation to visit the young man's home. They both had their photographs taken on the coaster, and later he received a copy with a very nice letter.

After his leave at home, which he enjoyed immensely, having a great time with his young son, he returned to his ship on a Tyne and Tees coaster from Newcastle Quay, accompanied by his wife and son. German ratings were signed on at Bremen to make up the crew, and Tom was surprised to see so many men come down for thirty jobs. Nevertheless they were all civil and orderly, so Tom and the Second Engineer picked their men for the following voyage, a voyage which was similar to their last one.

The ship was undergoing dry-docking and repairs at Bremen, so Tom and his wife were able to have a nice time at that port.

Here, also, the Captain was relieved by an older Master, who took the ship from Bremen to New York. This was in August 1927. The Second

Officer was relieved, too, and a very old friend of Tom's joined the ship in that capacity. Tom stayed on as requested, which suited him, as his wife and he had purchased a new house, which required mortgage.

All went well with the ship, and she made another voyage as before, these voyages taking five to six months. Once she went back to New York with a load of linseed, then back to the Plate and home again.

On the Bremen voyage she came back to Bremen from the River Plate, but from there the *African Prince* came to the River Tyne for three weeks lay up. The German crew were paid off there, and sent back home, and from then on British crews were carried. The ship did the usual run again, but came back to Liverpool. That was in June 1928. This next voyage took the ship to the Mediterranean. She had a fairly good cargo out, but not much homewards, Glasgow being the port she returned to.

On Tom's last voyage the ship returned from the River Plate and paid off at Liverpool, where she went through a special survey, which was due every four years. Tom had joined the ship at the completion of the last survey, so he had sailed four years in the *African Prince*. The ship was in good condition, and the surveyors congratulated Tom on keeping her so. They could not find any defects anywhere and all holds were well painted out. Usually a ship shows some signs of deterioration and must be brought up to standard again, this being over the half period of her expected life, but every part was in good shape, including masts and standing rigging, and when the survey was over a certificate was granted by Lloyds, which put a feather in Tom's hat.

The Marine Superintendent being on board, he mentioned that it might be time for Tom to have a change of ships for further experience towards a Master's berth, and word came from London for him to join the *Egyptian Prince*, a Mediterranean ship, so he went there for three voyages.

Chapter 14

THE PRINCE LINE NOW HAD FIVE NEW SHIPS, with motor engines, with speeds of fifteen and a half knots, doing a regular three weeks' service from New York on the round the world service. Each had a deadweight lifting power of 10,700 tons, and being specially built for that service they had many compartments for stowing the delicate cargoes. Cargoes with their own particular smells could be stowed without contamination from each other. In addition, they had large tanks for carrying liquid cargoes, each tank holding five hundred tons. Cargoes such as latex, palm oil and coconut oil could be carried.

In all they could carry a wider range, of very payable cargoes, than the old general purpose ships such as Tom had sailed in previously. He was taken off the *Egyptian Prince* and sent to New York to join one of these new ships, the *Javanese Prince*. He was signed on on 13 May 1930, and to be Chief Officer of one of those ships meant an extra seven pounds per month.

She had quite a large crew of Asiatics, there being twenty-five Malays under the Chief Officer, four quartermasters, a Serang and Tindel and the rest sailors. In the engine room they had Indians, about nineteen of them, and the catering department were Goanese Indians, about fifteen in number.

As usual when Tom joined a ship, he found out things for himself. This was a two years' contract, each voyage being about four months and a few days, New York to New York. He was beginning to know New York better than his home town. The Captain, John Smith, was a fine man, and the Second and Third Officers were good chaps too. She loaded the usual cargoes for the Far East via Los Angeles. The port of Los Angeles was only officially opened in 1929, and nothing but flat sandy ground met the eye for miles on first viewing the surrounding landscape.

The ship proceeded on her way across the Pacific Ocean to Yokohama, where there was no waiting about as the Japs were hard workers and soon had the cargo attended to. Kobe was the next port, which was more or less the same as Yokohama, and from there she sailed for Shanghai and so to Hong Kong. Small amounts of New York cargo started to be loaded at this port. The days of shipping case oil out to China had ended as the lamps of China had turned to electricity. The shopkeepers of Hong Kong

SS *Javanese Prince.* Swimming pool on deck.

liked brilliant lighting, so they used the highest power lamps, and, viewed from the ship, the hillside over the town of Victoria was closely dotted all over with brilliant lights, like the heavens with their stars on a dark clear night.

From Hong Kong the ship sailed for Manila in the Phillippines, and there loaded about a thousand tons of coconut oil in two of the deep tanks. Going on from there to Davao in South Mindanao Islands she loaded bales

SS *Javanese Prince.* Off Iloillo, Phillipines.

of hemp for making manila rope. The ports in Java were visited, Surabaya, Semarang and Batavia, the island then being under Dutch administration.

Then up to Singapore, Port Swettenham and Penang, loading all kinds of Far Eastern produce until the ship was practically full except for spaces left for cases of tea at Colombo. When the tea was loaded that was the final port, and she then sailed for Naples, via the Suez Canal. The ship carried a few passengers, mostly from Singapore. They were British people going home, so they would land at Naples. The ship would pick up some cargo there, then sail for Boston, USA, and to New York.

Tom did five voyages, lasting about twenty-five months, and then went home in one of the company's ships, which landed him back in the UK in September 1932.

About his last voyage on that ship, Tom was pleasantly surprised, on arriving at Shanghai, to find Captain Bill Paul and his wife visiting him. He had commenced his apprenticeship with Tom, and they had sailed together until Tom had been taken off at Brest with suspected appendicitis.

At Davao, Phillipines.

Bill was now Master of one of the Butterfield & Swire ships (China Coast Traders), and at that time he was running between Shanghai and Hankow, up the river Yangtze, on a passenger ship more like a ferry boat, which carried about three hundred Chinese.

They had a grand evening together at his home. Captain Paul's wife had been his boyhood sweetheart, and as he was spending the rest of his working life out on the China coast he had sent for her to come out and be married to him, and she had no regrets as they were very happy together.

Also on that last voyage, when the ship was in Hong Kong, tied up to buoys off the town, a police launch came alongside, amidst all the clatter and shouting of the various families on the Chinese junks alongside, and a stoutish chap dressed in the uniform of a police inspector, with his swagger stick under his arm, was soon jabbering away in the Chinese language to the several Chinese around him. Then Tom heard his name mentioned, so wondering what was wrong he called the inspector up to where he was watching from the fore part of the boat deck. When he came closer he recognised him as Olivier of the *Portuguese Prince*. They had been apprentices together, so they met with great joy. He had deserted the ship during the war and joined the Army. After the war he had gone out to the Far East and was sailing as Mate on a French sailing ship trading around the islands until it was wrecked.

SS *Javanese Prince*. Deck and engineer officers.

He was taken into Hong Kong as a shipwrecked mariner, then one day the padre of the Seamen's Mission, where he was staying, had suggested he join the police force, which he did, and never looked back. One never knows where one will end up on going to sea as an apprentice. He took Tom ashore to his home to meet his wife and two little girls, and they had a really good night together talking over their past lives. He also knew Captain Bill Paul, and they often met in Hong Kong.

On one voyage, on the way up the Pacific coast to Los Angeles, just before the ship crossed the Gulf of California, a cyclone, travelling up the coast at a great speed, overwhelmed the ship. Tom saw the barometer falling at about 4 a.m. when he came on watch, and heavy clouds were banking up to the south. As the glass continued to fall he called the Captain. Captain Smith came up on the bridge in his sleeping outfit and saw the conditions, and sent Tom down to the Chief Engineer to warn him of the coming of a storm, so that he could be prepared. He called the Chief Steward to get the few passengers out into the lounge fully dressed. The Captain had his wife with him on that voyage, so he told her to prepare herself.

The storm seemed to be travelling on the same track as the ship, as the barometer was falling fast, but the wind remained steady in direction and increasing in violence. From past experience Tom knew what to expect. It was now blowing at hurricane force, the spray off the sea was enveloping the ship and visibility was nil

The shrieking of the wind was tremendous, and suddenly it shifted with equal force to the beam from first being over the stern. A tremendous sea struck the starboard side and heeled the ship over, as it seemed, on her beam ends. It was fifty degrees by the clinometer.

The Captain lost his hold and shot right out of the wheelhouse on his back, the lee door being open. Tom followed suit, and grabbed the standard of the engine room telegraph as he went by, nearly pulling his arms out of their sockets.

The Captain crashed into the side of the bridge, which had glass windows, breaking much of the glass and knocking him out. The ship came back slowly to about fifteen degrees from upright, and Tom managed to drag the Captain into the wheelhouse, and with the first aid kit up on the bridge did his best to attend to severe cuts while the ship was being battered about. The engines were no use at all, as the oil was not getting to the machinery.

The Captain came to eventually, and the shrieking of the wind was gradually lessening. The wind shifted about 10 a.m. when the ship heeled over, and died down rapidly after 11 a.m. By 2 p.m. it was fine and clear, with little wind at all, but the ship retained the list of about ten degrees, as much cargo had shifted in the 'tween decks. Several heavy lifts of five to ten tons had broken their lashings and shot over to the low side when hit by the sea. Some had smashed the wooden 'tween hatches and stuck between the beams, but there was nothing Tom could do about that.

They were only two days from Los Angeles, however, the weather was now fine and no more cyclones would appear.

On arriving in port, the cargo was re-stowed by the stevedores, with the help of cranes and derricks. The ship also was taking full bunkers of diesel oil for the voyage as far as Port Said, filling the double bottom tanks as well as two of the deep tanks, and when she left Los Angeles she was properly stowed and ship-shape.

When crossing the Atlantic Ocean bound to Boston in January 1931, she met much heavy weather, and the Captain took the great circle track north of the Azores. For some time she had been running on one engine, as the other needed to change its jet valves. It was the 9th of the month, about 6 p.m., dark and stormy, and both engines were running again, when a freak sea, like a mountain, lifted itself up in front of the ship and she just dashed into it. Tom gazed at the whole of the fore deck taking gallons of water. She had struck with a proper shock blow, and was reduced in speed. When the water poured over the sides it carried away all the ventilators off the fore deck and they were extraordinarily big ones, too. The sea smashed in number one hatch and tons of water went down the hold. The Captain hove her to, and Tom got along to the fore deck and saw that the hatch had been split wide open, with all the beams twisted and hatch boards smashed and tarpaulins torn to shreds.

Tom called all hands out, as well as the Second and Third Officers, and gave them the job of getting the ventilator steel covers over the remaining coamings. The covers were available in the mast house. Tom and his men pulled up hatches from the 'tween decks and all spare hatch planks that could be found, then with a large double-ended saw he set them to sawing hatches and planks to fit the twisted beams. The night was dark and the ship was shipping water although she was hove to, while to make matters worse several barrels of oil under the forecastle head had broken and the oil was all over the deck, which made everything slippery.

In time the hatch was covered by the wooden makeshift hatches. Three new tarpaulins were taken out of the sail locker, and the hatch covered, with a certain amount of difficulty as the wind kept blowing them off. The hatch was battened down and well wedged, and the other officers had the ventilator coamings covered, so she was all right there. The hold had about a thousand tons of raw sugar in bags down below and the 'tween decks had cases of lemons from Naples, and much water went into that hold. The bilge pumps were kept going, but it was thought the sugar would soak up the sea water. Anyhow the ship was secure as far as she could be made so. When she reached New York for discharging the sugar, she was found to be much damaged; the twisted steel portable beams in the hatchway were repaired and new hatches made.

On another voyage, during the south-west monsoon period, the Goodyear Rubber people shipped a number of wild animals for New York, taking tigers and leopards, honey bears and enormous lizards about ten feet long from Sumatra. The tigers and leopards were, of course, in cages, and the lizards in crates. At Singapore about five hundred different species of tropical birds, monkeys of all types and several snakes from cobras to a large snake twenty-seven feet long coiled up in a box were taken aboard, and there was also a large crocodile.

Food was put aboard for them, but Tom's men had to feed them. Several bullocks were killed and shipped for that purpose.

They also had two baby orang-outangs and they were the cutest animals ever. Tom had a wire set up on each side of the after deck, the full length of the deck and about eight feet above it, to which the orang-outangs were attached by a chain so they had liberty to play on the whole deck within limits of their chain. Every time Tom went along they would jump into his arms to be nursed and then would jump up and grab his cap and off. It would happen every day; no doubt other members of the crew had the

SS *Javanese Prince.*
Author as Chief Officer,
resting.

same treatment, but it kept them exercised. He would go along to the other monkeys and talk to them – they finished up by shaking hands. Often such actions would cause a lot of jealousy among those animals not receiving notice.

Tom thought the monkeys looked really pathetic in cages just big enough for them. They also shipped snakes and lizards of about 6 to 8 feet in overall length and proportioned accordingly. These were in flat cases and stowed around the masts. The snakes often hatched eggs and then the little fellows would easily get out of cages and they would be found everywhere. One snake was 47 feet long but coiled up in a box. This one had been fed before it was shipped and was good for a couple of months of hibernation. It was measured on the dock by the zoo people.

The birds were stowed under the forecastle head, and it was a job to feed and water them alone. They were protected from the weather, but the monsoon did not help in any way.

One man was in charge of this wild stock and most of it arrived safely at New York and was placed on the dock on arrival for inspection by the Zoo officials.

Tom was the only officer on board that night as he had given the others permission to have a night off. The Second Officer of one of the other ships came aboard to have a late meal with him, being a good friend of Tom's. Before going into the dining-room Tom and his friend were having a little drop of gin together and a yarn about old times when the dock watchman knocked at the door and asked if Tom would see a newspaper reporter who was at the top of the dock. Tom did not want to see any more newspapermen that day as he had had many curious people on board and was becoming tired of the continual questions.

The watchman went away and Tom thought no more about him, but later on a gentle knock was heard on the door and Tom investigated, to find a charming young lady who produced a newspaper reporter's card. Tom could not exactly turn her away, and it happened that he was just going along to the dining saloon for his evening meal, so he gave her an invitation to come along too and make a threesome.

All went well. She gathered all the information she wanted, and as a grand finale they visited the animals on the dock. They were very nervous and kicking up a hideous row. Tom knew that the last cage in the row contained a very sick tiger, so when they came to it Tom said as a joke that he would mesmerise this one. After doing a few antics, he scratched the animal behind the ears, then left it, knowing the poor thing had not long to live. The young lady went off to her office and so the day ended.

In the morning Tom was presented with a free copy of the *Brooklyn Times* and there found on the front page in large print 'Mate of Zoo Ship

A painting of SS *Javanese Prince* by Bruce Clark.

Tames Tiger by Mesmerism', with a column and a half of newsprint for good measure. When the chaps on the dock read that they started pulling all kinds of tricks to avoid meeting Tom face to face in case he hypnotised them. Tom knew them all as he had worked for many years with them on various ships, they being regular gangs. He began receiving telephone calls from people wanting him to speak at meetings, and some even came to the ship and produced their visiting cards. It took some time for all this to blow over, and he had to stand much leg-pulling from his fellow officers.

The sick tiger had been shot dead the next day. It was found, too, that the crocodile had been dead for some time, and the large snake was stretched out on the dock and measured. The Zoo officials had taken over the animals and birds, and Tom was glad to see the last of them.

Every voyage on that ship was very interesting to Tom. One voyage they picked up Claudette Colbert and Norman Foster, the film stars, as passengers from Shangai to Surabaya. Believe it or not Tom had never heard of them before, but afterwards when visiting the cinema in Singapore he saw them in a film.

Chapter 15

Tom had three months at home at the latter end of 1932 and enjoyed being with his wife and family. He now had two sons, aged eight and four, and was very proud of them. After being away from home for a couple of years it was strange coming amongst them again. It was not good to leave one's family for such long periods, but when Tom saw the number of people out of work, who had been like this for years, he felt that he had done the best thing for his wife and sons.

Fortunately his next job was to look after a ship which was laid up in Rothesay Bay in the Firth of Clyde. This ship was the *African Prince* on which Tom had served for four years as Chief Officer. Close by was the *Siberian Prince*, another ship on which Tom had served. He joined his ship at the end of 1932 and stayed there for one year. He was on his own as shipkeeper except when an engineer came every fortnight to turn the engine a little and check things over. The engineer did this job on several of the company's ships laid up in the Gairloch.

Tom had his wife and younger son with him most of the time, and his elder son came up there on his school holidays, so it was nearly as good as being at home.

The Prince of Wales, afterwards the Duke of Windsor, came to visit Rothesay on a destroyer; being holiday time it was quite a day for the local people. The Prince Line Company's mark was the Prince of Wales feathers on each side of the funnel. Tom received word from the owners to have the funnel painted and the ship freshened up for the visit of Royalty, which he did anyhow; as he had been already on this job seven months she was fairly clean; the Company sent him all the paint he needed.

When the warship was taking the Prince of Wales back to Gourock for the train to London, it steamed around the five ships laid up in Rothesay Bay. Tom and his wife were standing on the bridge deck when it came in close to their ship; they stood at attention and saluted, the Prince saluted back to them. Everyone on the ship received a letter from the Prince thanking them, and in Tom's he particularly mentioned that he was pleased to see his feathers decorating the funnel. Tom sent that letter back to the Superintendent's Department, London. He might have kept it as one does not get a letter like that every day of the week.

That job finished when the company decided to sell several of the ships laid up in that area. The *Siberian Prince* had to go to dry-dock at Greenock to be surveyed and sold to a Greek firm, so Tom went over to assist in the work. It took at least eight hours to take in the anchors as the anchor chains were twisted around each other. They were sealed with barnacles and sea growth, and the turns could not be taken out as the sea growth kept them knitted together. The chain could only be hove in about six feet at a time to clear this growth off and even then the anchors were locked together, so she went to the dock like that.

After seeing some of the ships sold, Tom had Christmas and New Year at home, then joined the *Stuart Prince* at Manchester for the Mediterranean trade as Chief Officer. The *Stuart Prince* was a fairly old ship, the old three island type. The pay on her was not so good, being eighteen pounds, ten shillings per month as Chief Officer, but at least Tom was employed. The Captain, Fred Pearson, was an old friend of Tom's, and the Chief Engineer, Mr MacArthur, had been on her since she first came out.

She traded to the Near East ports as Tom had done before on other ships of that type. Conditions were changing rapidly as regards to Palestine, which gave the ships good outward bound cargoes of coloured cement and reinforcing iron for Haifa and Tel Aviv. These towns were building up rapidly and the harbour of Haifa was nearly completed. It was protected from winds in any direction off the sea by two magnificent breakwaters, and splendid wharves and warehouses were rising on the new quays.

Tel Aviv, too, was quite a city. Beautiful hotels and dwellings could now be seen from the sea, where there had been only barren land a few years ago. The beach appeared to be a holiday resort, as coloured umbrellas could be seen dotted all over, together with crowds of semi-naked humans. It was not a protected harbour like Haifa. Ships anchored off there at about half a mile distance in order to discharge machinery for the power station, as Tom's ship did, discharging twenty-ton generators. When the wind rose above force four it was time to heave up and stand off the land two or three miles.

Jaffa was only a mile further south, and was still an Arab port or anchorage for loading citrus fruit. The Jewish population of Palestine were certainly altering the coastline's face. The British were building Haifa port and Tom got to know some of the men employed on the building; in fact, the chief diver doing the dockside wall was from the same part of the River Tyne as he was.

As is still the case today, much trouble was going on between the Jews and Arabs. Jews were landing in hordes from old ships which had brought them from Spain and other Mediterranean ports and countries, and the British Army was out there and were kept very busy. A battleship of the Royal Navy was moored stern on to the quay, and the railway was being operated by Naval men.

The port was officially opened by the British Governor on one of the Prince Line ships. The British had an oil pipeline direct from the Persian Gulf which ended at Haifa. This would have been a great saver of time if left to operate, but the Arabs found satisfaction in occasionally blowing it up. They must have served with Lawrence of Arabia.

Citrus fruit was now growing in great quantities, and being shipped by the Jews out of Haifa. The fertilisers that were being shipped out from the ICI at Billingham were making more land productive. The *Stuart Prince* took out a full cargo of bagged fertiliser from Billingham a few times when the ICI was in its infancy, but Tom thought the fruit was not so juicy as that shipped by the Arabs of the old school.

The Jews were administering the settled parts of Palestine from Haifa, and seemed to Tom strongly Communistic in their thinking, as all were equal in their determination to make a living out of the land. A number of old friends among the Arabs were very bitter about the Jews, for once they got in they were ruthless in taking over the lands of the Arabs. No doubt the Arab population had steadier employment under the Jewish order, but it was much more exacting than their old way of life.

Cyprus, too, was beginning fruit production on a larger scale, and many retired people from the British Army made their homes on the island. Land was cheap and so were houses. The cultivation of citrus fruit brought their fruit up to a very high standard, equal to that of Jaffa in quantity if not in quality.

Outside the fruit season, the *Stuart Prince* often came back light ship. Sometimes she would call into Almeria, Spain, for kegs of grapes. She made one voyage, after discharge, to the Black Sea, going to Theodosiya in the Crimea to load a full cargo of grain. Shifting boards were required to be fitted for that cargo, and none were on the ship, so some had to be bought, but they could not be got anywhere. At Theodosiya a trainload of sliced tree trunks was offered, and the Captain and Tom had a look at them. They were about eighteen inches to two feet wide and three and a half inches thick, with the bark still on the outer edges. It was decided to take them as the time of the grain charter was running out. With such irregular boards, dunnage boards would have to be nailed over the landing edges to make them grain-tight.

They got them alongside. These boards were in twenty-foot lengths, and very heavy. Tom got started, and the carpenter was instructed to take number one hold, Tom took number two and three holds, the Second Officer number four hold, and the Old Man had a go at number five to erect an amidship fore and aft wooden division right through the holds of the ship. When completed and made grain-tight this would prevent the grain cargo from shifting in heavy weather, with the possibility of capsizing the ship. Working right through twenty-four hours the work was completed. Everyone worked hard, and Tom was swinging about like a monkey, as were those in the other holds, placing the boards and setting up uprights and shores.

They made it with their Notice of Readiness in time to save the charter and load the ship. The feeders were left until later. These were filled with grain to feed the lower holds where slackness showed on the voyage through being shaken down or through poor trimming. The Russians were surprised and pleased that the shifting boards were finished in time, observing that the Captain and officers worked as hard as the crew, if not harder, to keep all holds going with the help of the engineers. The armed guard was then taken off the gangway. This was in early 1936.

At the beginning of this voyage Tom applied to the Port of London Authority for an assistant dockmaster's position in the London Docks. The grain cargo was discharged into the Co-operative Society Flour Mills at Trafford Park, Manchester, within two or three days, leaving the shifting boards standing. Now no nails except for dunnage light boards were used to secure the boards and they would all collapse when the shores were lifted out. The ship immediately left Manchester to bunker at Partington, further down the canal. There Tom received a forwarded letter from his wife to say that the Port of London Authority wished him to attend an interview at London on the following Monday. As it was now Friday, Tom telephoned the London office from Partington and put his situation to them as the ship was leaving for Antwerp that night. No time was lost from the Superintendent's department, who immediately instructed the Liverpool office to send a Chief Officer from a ship laid up there, the *Cyprian Prince*, and they sent him up to Partington by car, so Tom was relieved that night to go home and later to keep his appointment on the Monday with the PLA. Tom met with doubtful looks when he arrived home, as the position did not look very bright to his wife. Anyhow, he went down, and he and six other chaps were interviewed by the Board one at a time, Tom being the first.

After a while five were dropped, which left Tom and a Chief Officer from another line. Then Tom was dropped, so he did not get the job as an assistant dockmaster. He reported to the Head Office of the Prince Line, thinking this was the last time he would do so. But they told him to join the ship his relief had left in Liverpool. Also they said if they had only known of his application beforehand they could have done something about it so he would probably have had the job. Well, that was very nice; and he went home for a night and then to Liverpool. The Spanish Civil War was on the verge of breaking out, and ships were beginning to move slowly. Tom was shipkeeping for about one month, then word came to get the ship ready for sea and engage some men from the shipping office, so things were starting to look brighter. Tom had the derricks re-rigged and the life-saving appliances, including the boats, set up ready for BOT survey. Another friend of Tom's joined, Captain Marshall, and the crew signed on at the shipping office. All was ready when Tom got a telegram to go to Dartmouth and do the same to a ship lying in the river Dart. He was sorry to leave this Captain, but he went down to the Dart and found the laid-up ship, the *Corsican Prince*, tied to buoys in the middle of the river.

Next day he hired a batch of men and started to prepare the vessel for future service. The Chief Engineer was there, and he had to get the engines ready for use, which meant that the other engineers were on their way down.

The ship had been employed previously on the New York–South America trade, but had been laid up in the Dart for the past two years. She was rather a smart-looking ship with plenty of teak wood and varnish about her. This had all been smothered in linseed oil and took some cleaning off.

Tom was then advised that the Captain and crew from the ship he had just left were coming down to join the *Corsican Prince*, so this ship was going to sail and the other one would be held back for some time. In due course they all arrived on board, all happy because they were sure of this ship sailing. After going over the ship with the Bosun and carpenter they soon put things in order then the articles were opened at the shipping office and all signed on.

In the course of a few days she was taken around to Falmouth to dry-dock, to have all the necessary work done on the bottom, including taking the propeller off for inspection.

When all had been attended to she went over to Antwerp to commence loading, then eventually sailed for the Mediterranean ports of the Near East. Tom had a good crew on this ship, so he was happy to carry on.

After the outward cargo was discharged she carried sheep from Alexandretta to Haifa, which were run off at that port in a few hours. Now the ship had to be cleaned and sweetened. It seemed that all the Arab labour in the port must have been used to do this job. She was on the berth at Jaffa the next day to load citrus fruit.

Many happy days were spent on that ship, such as lying quietly in Famagusta harbour for a few days, waiting for a turn to load citrus fruit at Jaffa or Haifa, as in those days Cyprus was trouble-free. The people may have been poor as far as money was concerned, but they had plenty of the good things off the land, and led a very simple life. Every day was

SS *Corsican Prince.*
Author and Third
Officer visiting old
Roman tombs in
Alexandria.

as quiet as a Sunday in Famagusta harbour, as Tom's ship was the only one there.

Tom received permission to employ shore labour to scale all the deck houses, so he eventually got the ship up to peak condition and looking as smart as she had been in her pre-laid-up days. Tom was a great believer in the old saying, 'It pays to advertise', so he kept his ship spick and span both inside and out, as that was the only way to show it off.

After twelve months on this ship doing eight voyages, they arrived in Manchester during February 1938 and found that the ship had been sold to the French. After the French had inspected her their representatives seemed to be very pleased, so she was taken over by the French company without further ado. Tom was instructed to take a week's leave and join another ship in London of the same class. This was the *Sicilian Prince*, of which he was to be Chief Officer.

He duly joined the ship and introduced himself to the Captain. He had never sailed with this gentleman, but Tom had nothing to grumble about as all went along merrily, with big cargoes being loaded outwards. Malta was being well provided for. The Spanish Civil War was at its height and anything could happen. The trading ports were more or less the same.

Alexandria offered many attractions for the wanderer. The Chief Engineer was a good companion for Tom, and many a Sunday they

The author and Second Engineer visiting Cyprus.

wandered up the canal banks, watching the sailing craft bringing goods and produce from up the Nile.

The zoo with its gardens was worth a visit at any time. An old washerwoman often brought beautiful roses to decorate Tom's cabin, and the perfume of these was out of this world. It was a pleasure, too, in the Botanical Gardens, where the scent of different flowers was very powerful.

Visits to the Museum were worthwhile, for the objects to be seen there brought the age of the ancient Kings of Egypt very close to the observer.

An old Sudanese, who had been a sergeant in the British Sudanese army, ran a taxi service. He had only one car of ancient origin, but he was a most obliging man and could be hired all day, so he was used on a Sunday by Tom and the Chief Engineer.

In the evenings after work finished on the ship, the small boat belonging to the ship would be rigged for a sail in the outer harbour, and the evening would be spent boating and swimming. A call was generally made to the swimming club, which was situated on a small island in the outer harbour, and there a glass of cold beer could be enjoyed.

So life was not all hard work during those days in Alexandria. Inside the docks was the Seamen's Mission where there was a good billiards table, while soft drinks and tea could be had at any time. Tom was asked, during the course of his visits there, if he would like to take the job of Superintendent of that outfit, but he could not see his way clear to do so.

Just outside the dock gate was a bar run by a Greek gentleman which went under the title used by all and sundry as 'Greek George's'. There were always two or three ships in port of the same company, or other regular callers, and at about 9 p.m. there would always be one or two men off each ship leaning on the bar counter, having a glass before going to bed and discussing the topics of the day. In those days beer and intoxicating waters were strictly forbidden on board ship. In any case, no one could afford such indulgence.

Those months before the Second World War were very peaceful, although in 1938 a war scare came along, and Tom fitted up gripping spars on the lifeboat davits in order that the boats could be carried outboard and gripped to the spar on a slip hook so that they could be easily lowered at sea in case of attack.

All officers were expected to attend classes once a year on convoy procedure and gunnery practice, to be ready for any emergency. Courses were conducted on HMS *Satellite* on the river Tyne, which Tom attended if at home for any period.

On the Mediterranean trading ships, the atmosphere on the ship was much more friendly than on ships away from home for long periods.

During the winter months the weather could really be bad at sea. Sometimes on a voyage home with fruit from Jaffa on a ten-knot ship, with a strong westerly wind all the way through the Mediterranean, the passage to Gibraltar could take ten days, which was about twice the time it should be in fine weather.

Tom was beginning to wonder when he was going to be promoted to Master, as he had now been a Chief Officer for over thirteen years. During his twenty-five years at sea he had had experience in all trades and took the good with the bad in his stride. A few promotions had been going, but Tom had never been around to catch on to any, so he did become a little despondent now and again. Now he had three fine sons and was extremely fond of them. His ambition was to give them all a University education. The time had passed when he was glad just to be in a job, during the dark years between the wars. Now he was forty years of age, and something must turn up soon or he would try elsewhere, but to be ashore looking elsewhere costs money, and none came in when off a ship.

The Chief Engineer was a very religious man, and was a great influence on Tom, so he suggested Tom might do a little praying at night before going to bed. This Tom did, and received some comfort through this.

The year 1939 was clipping off the months, and it came to pass that a ship was lying at Middlesbrough loading cargo for the Mediterranean ports. It was during the mid-day meal when the dock office reported he was wanted on the telephone from Head Office. Tom went down to the dock office and picked up the 'phone. A voice on the other end said he was to go as Master of the SS *Syrian Prince*, now lying at Manchester, and he would join her on Monday 1 May.

Needless to say, Tom was elated, for at last he had reached his goal. The day was Friday and the Captain released him immediately, so he packed up and signed off the articles.

Everyone on board gave him cheery good wishes and a real good send-off. He took the train for home, and there he told his wife the good news. Everybody was very pleased, for the financial position looked more promising now.

On the Monday he joined the ship and found his old friend the *Corsican Prince* was there. *Syrian Prince* was a fairly new one, about three thousand tons deadweight, which was not very big; in fact it was the smallest ship he had been on, but it was a start. He had his name put on the ship's register at the Custom House, so he was now Master. Up to the tailor's he went, and had his three bands taken off his uniform sleeves and the four bands of Master put on to replace them.

A new outfit could come later on when he was established.

Chapter 16

THE *Syrian Prince* was on the Mediterranean trade, so now Tom would be calling at those ports through the Master's eyes, and probably when in port would go off to those mysterious places with the agent called 'the office'. A new life was opening up for Tom. He was addressed as Captain Sloane, and he had his officers to report to him on cargo working and such matters as required his attention.

About twice a week he would make an inspection of all crew accommodation in company with the heads of departments to see that all was kept in good order. Being a good Chief Officer himself he knew what to look for. Now he need not dirty his hands and must always be dressed formally. The Chief Steward was an old-timer; in fact, he had been in that job when Tom was an apprentice. He was a good man, and Tom learned a lot from him about his department.

The Chief Engineer had been Second Engineer with Tom when he was Chief Officer on the *Stuart Prince*, so they were old friends. Many times had they dashed away on Sunday in a home port, on a railway excursion, home for a few hours, the cost being nine shillings return from London and four and six return from Manchester. They would catch the train at about 9 a.m. and return about midnight from Newcastle, arriving at the ship at 7 o'clock on the Monday morning, ready for the day's duties, possibly walking five or six miles from the railway station to the ship in the docks. With those memories he was sure his friend the Chief Engineer would co-operate with the new Master.

They made two voyages up the Mediterranean and back home, and Tom's wife would visit the ship in a home port. At the end of the second voyage the ship was in the Manchester dry dock, and Tom had taken his wife and young son on a trip to Southport, the day being Sunday. On returning by train, being rather late at night, it was noticed that the lighting in the carriages was by blue globes which made it very low and gave him the 'willies'. On arriving on board ship he was met by the new Chief Officer, Mr King, whom he had not been expecting till Monday. There were three other gentlemen with him, and the time was about midnight about one week before war was declared. The three gentlemen were from the Admiralty, one being a Commander RNR in uniform, who had been recently called back to the Royal Navy, and the other two from the dockyard at Devonport. Tom was told the ship had been taken over by the Admiralty and he had to get round to Devonport as quickly as possible. Just then a Customs officer came on board with a message to the effect that war was imminent. Tom had received instructions while on convoy course about such a message.

Now the ship was in dry dock at Manchester and six plates were off the sides of her. First Tom had to go over to the dock office, where there was nobody except the watchman about, but with the impressive gentlemen behind Tom he was given use of the 'phone. He was given a number to call, which was for the Admiralty in London, and a voice came back telling Tom to get the plates back as quickly as possible and sail for Devonport. The Admiralty would re-dock the ship and do all the necessary work to suit their requirements, which were extensive.

Next Tom had to telephone the dry dock manager, which no doubt got him out of bed. When Tom told him the news he was very annoyed, saying he must see the Superintendent first. As the Naval officer was listening, he told Tom to inform the manager he had to take his orders from the Master of the ship, as the Admiralty was in control of her.

Next on the card was to find accommodation for the three Admiralty officers, which was soon accomplished as there were plenty of available passenger rooms.

Next morning at 8.00 sharp they were on the ball again and soon got things moving. Everything was taken out of the hands of the Company's

SS *Syrian Prince.*

representatives, and the ship was prepared for sea. A crew had to be signed on, which took all the next day. She then sailed on the Tuesday from the canal. At Eastham Locks another Royal Navy officer came on board with a bag full of Naval books for signalling purposes. He also had instructions to steam without navigation lights to Devonport.

The *Syrian Prince* duly arrived there, to be taken in hand by the dockyard people. All electric wiring was stripped out of the holds, the cargo gear was renewed and all the derricks tested to fifty per cent overload. Awnings were fitted all over the ship, together with awnings over the side to keep the holds cool.

All the holds were fitted out with wood in so-called bins for carrying ammunition to ships of war at sea. When that was completed, she went up-river to the ammunition base and loaded up. During this time war had been declared and the whole place was blacked out at night.

Captain Tom Sloane had to sign a Charter of the Admiralty and she sailed on 27 September 1939, with sealed orders.

Tom remembers that night of sailing. It was raining heavily, and they had to anchor in Plymouth Sound first to wait until a convoy passed. Four ships were going out, the *Syrian Prince* being the leader. About midnight the anchor was hove up and Tom took her out between the piers. It was as black as could be. On getting outside, a destroyer came up alongside and told Tom to ease down as the other three ships were late in coming. Tom could see the dark shapes of the convoy ships as they were passing, so they trailed them until daylight.

Next morning they formed up in the convoy, with two or three destroyers as escorts. After three days in company with the rest the *Syrian Prince* was signalled to proceed on her own to her destination. The sealed orders were opened and it was found that they had to go to Halifax, Nova Scotia. They were given the course to take, so that if anything happened on the passage the Admiralty would know what track the ship was on.

She had been fitted with a twelve-pounder gun on the stern. A Naval staff consisted of one Chief Petty Officer, one Sergeant of Marines and one Naval Signalman. The crew had attended instructional courses on gunnery, gas warfare and fire drills.

After an uneventful passage they arrived at Halifax. At that period the Canadian Navy were calling up all reserves, mostly British Naval officers who had gone into business in Canada.

The Prince Line had an office in Halifax, so Tom reported there, and the manager of the office was very good in helping Tom to make his introductions to the Canadian Naval authorities.

The manager had gone over to the Ministry of Shipping and was acquainted with dockyard routine. An elderly officer, wearing the uniform of a commander, took over the care of the *Syrian Prince*, and had her tied up at a small wharf in Bedford Basin, attached to the ammunition base. There three destroyers (Canadian) received their stock of ammunition from the *Syrian Prince*, and a certain amount was landed at the base. They were under the Blue Ensign now and had become part of the Naval set-up. Everything seemed so unreal to Tom, without the hustle and bustle of a general cargo ship.

After a few days there Captain Tom was ordered to Bermuda, and one hundred miles out she passed through the tail end of a hurricane. Being a little ship she jumped about a great deal on the high, heavy seas, but fortunately no damage to the ship occurred, nor to the dangerous cargo she was carrying.

On arriving at Bermuda she was taken to the dockyard and one of their tugs took the ship there and tied up to the quayside. More ammunition was taken out there, a regular ammunition supply officer being at this base.

The Admiral in charge of Bermuda was the man who directed the ship. Tom was invited to lunch with him at Government House, so he got to know who he was dealing with. After a few days in Bermuda, which was a nice break for Tom's crew as they were invited to the Naval Mess, she was ordered to Trinidad in the West Indies.

Arriving there she was taken into the port, which had not long been completed with wharves and breakwaters as well as warehouses. While there she found herself storing up five British destroyers. HMS *Hardy* was the flagship, and these very same destroyers attacked a similar number of German destroyers in Narvik, Norway, badly damaging the same and sinking some of them. Tom met the Captain of the *Hardy* and had him aboard for lunch. By this time Tom was getting to know the work he was engaged upon. The *Syrian Prince* then went over to Jamaica, seeing the same destroyers again. The Prince Line's agent attended on the ship at each port. As far as stores for the ship's use were concerned, the Chief Steward saw to it that they were amply supplied. Being an old servant of the company, Tom had great faith in him.

From Jamaica the *Syrian Prince* went back to Bermuda, and after a week or so there, news came through about the *Graf Spee* affair off the River Plate. The *Syrian Prince* was made ready to proceed south to supply more ammunition to the three British warships engaged in the battle. They were just on the point of leaving when news came to the effect that the *Graf Spee* had made for Montevideo, so off they went south, but it would take some time to reach the position, unless the warships came to meet them. Not long after leaving she was called back to port as the *Graf Spee* had scuttled herself.

Back in Bermuda the *Syrian Prince* was ordered to off-load all the remaining ammunition and then proceed to Halifax for convoy home. Before leaving Bermuda about a thousand tons of old anchor chain, old-time guns and such-like from the old dockyard, was loaded.

After clearing St David's Head, a message came to the *Syrian Prince* from the shore signal station by morse lamp to proceed to a rendezvous about a day's run north, where the same group of destroyers had captured a German cargo ship. The *Syrian Prince* was instructed to bring the crew back to Bermuda, with the assistance of one of the destroyers.

On arriving at the rendezvous, however, no signs could be seen of any craft at all, so Tom decided to carry on to Halifax. It was now approaching Christmas, and the ship arrived off Sambro Lightship in thick fog on the 23rd. It was so thick that they were fortunate to see the lightship, passing very close. From there it was a straight course to Chebucto Head, about twelve miles away. The fog signal on the steam whistle was kept going, with one blast every two minutes, then suddenly a siren was heard on the starboard bow. The ship was stopped, and the Second Officer and Tom were peering and listening out into the fog, when silently and majestically out of the gloom came a huge battleship. It was a French ship, and she slid into the fog again as she passed, followed by a large passenger ship, then came more and more of them, slipping out of the fog and disappearing again as they passed. This was the first convoy of Canadian Forces going over to Britain, and it was indeed quite a sight seeing all those big ships silently slipping by.

Tom eventually got his ship into port, where the pilot boarded, and she was taken alongside one of the general cargo wharves. They discovered here that an American warship had taken the German crew into their port, much against the wishes of our people. Tom's ship was flying the Blue Ensign with an anchor at the fly. This was the ensign allotted to her on being taken over by the Admiralty.

Now she had no ammunition on board, only the thousand tons of old chains and guns. The Ministry of Shipping at Halifax decided to put further blocks of steel on board to load her down to her marks, but on such a small ship that was not good as it could only go into the bottom of the ship and lower the centre of gravity to such an extent that she would be in a dangerous condition in a heavy sea. Lighter cargo was needed in the upper decks to raise the centre of gravity to make the ship manageable.

Those old boys in the Ministry took some talking over to Tom's way of thinking, but eventually they gave him foodstuff, such as bags of flour and sides of bacon, well wrapped, of course, so that the ship had all her space used and in a reasonable condition of stowage. The old iron itself would make the ship fairly stiff.

When she was loaded in the bins with ammunition down the holds she went into Bedford Basin to wait for the convoy to form up. The date to leave was 6 January 1940, and the snow was coming down heavily. On the afternoon before sailing all Masters of ships in the Basin had to go to Admiralty House in the dockyard for the convoy conference, and several motor boats came to the ships to take the Masters ashore.

Before his ship went out to anchorage, Tom made friends with a youngish American Captain of an oil tanker. They always had lunch together, and would probably go to a movie in the afternoon, as the weather was too cold to wander far afield.

At the conference chambers in Admiralty House there were twenty-one Masters of ships around the table, all in civvies. The Chairman was a Canadian commander, and also at the table was the Captain of the escort, HMS *Revenge*, a huge battleship. He was a hard-bitten old boy, ready for anything. Then there was the Commodore of the Convoy, who was a retired Admiral. This gentleman was in full charge of the convoy going across to Britain. On a raised platform at the side were several gentlemen of high rank, the principal being Lord Tweedsmuir, otherwise John Buchan, Governor-General of Canada. Such a setting would have made an excellent picture.

As the Chairman was giving the instructions, a Naval officer was writing across a blackboard with a piece of chalk, to indicate how the ships would form up when out at sea, each ship being given a two-flag signal which indicated its number in the convoy. The first flag was the number of the column he had to be in, and the second the number and position in that column.

Tom recognised the officer doing the blackboard work as an ex-Prince Line officer. He was a lieutenant then, but soon rose to be Captain, RNR, taking convoys across.

The Commodore chose the ship on which he was to conduct operations and they made the little *Syrian Prince* vice-Commodore, so Tom was the man to take over, should anything happen to the Commodore. In any case he had to lead the Liverpool-bound ships into port when the convoy broke up in the Irish Sea, as some were going to Glasgow.

After the conference the Chairman gave the Masters a couple of bottles of beer because he was the host and was extending the hospitality of the Canadian Royal Navy. He also happened to own a brewery.

It was quite dark, somewhere about 6 p.m., and snowing heavily when the shipmasters left the building and made their way to the boats to be taken off to their ships, with their instructions in their attaché cases.

There were four motor boats to take off the Masters. Tom took his seat with four others, and the talk was about tomorrow's sailing at 6 a.m. and the conference in general. The coxswain knew the ships they were going to, but he had a job to see his way on account of the heavy snow. He pulled up at one ship alongside a rope ladder and shouted that this was Tom's ship. Tom could not look up because of the snow, and all he saw was about two steps of the ladder and a square foot of steel plating.

He said goodnight, and got on to the ladder, the boat pushing off at the same time and being soon lost in the snow. Tom started climbing, then realised he was on the wrong ship, as his own ship had little freeboard, while this one was, or seemed to be, as high out of the water as the Empire State Building.

Arriving at the top, as it was no use staying down there on the ladder, the officer thought he was the pilot to take the ship out in the morning, and Tom had difficulty in describing his dismal adventure of being put on board the wrong ship. In due course the boat came back after delivering the other Masters, with the proper Master of this ship.

Tom dropped down over the side after telling the Captain he wanted overtime for climbing halfway to heaven. He was soon delivered to his own ship, and was glad to get to bed after issuing orders for a 5.30 a.m. start. He had no pilot, as there were only twenty for twenty-one ships, but the others had.

Next morning it was still snowing heavily. Tom waited until the tail end and so left with the others, single line ahead. Outside, by the Sambro, they formed up in four columns with Tom at the tail of the right-hand side and not far away from the battleship. Three Canadian destroyers were cruising around, searching for submarines, but left them off Newfoundland. The speed was seven and a half knots officially. The snow was still falling, and was likely to do so all the way, as a north-east wind was blowing and the convoy was going further north.

The *Syrian Prince's* Naval signalman was kept busy at all times, signalling to the *Revenge*, as they were receiving information on minefields being laid in the Irish Sea, particularly a mine area on the approaches to Liverpool, outside the ten-fathom line. The approach now was to make for the Preston lightship and from there come south inside the ten-fathom line to the Bar lightship off the entrance to the river Mersey. This Tom had to have verified, as he was leading the Liverpool section of the convoy.

The weather was not too bad on the way across, but now and again the seas were very high for his small ship, and twice he had to heave to for a few hours or else have had the hatches stove in, but he caught up with the convoy the next day. It snowed all the way, and in the heavy squalls visibility was very poor.

At noon each day every ship had to hoist its latitude and longitude signals in the international code. The mean of these would be taken as official, which the Commodore would hoist. Sometimes they obtained solar or stellar observations when the sky and horizon were clear enough.

In course of time the convoy arrived off the south of Ireland. The home escort met the convoy, and as these three destroyers took over, the *Revenge* left for her base at Devonport.

No land was sighted, as the visibility was still very poor, and no navigation lights on the coast were lit. Coming up the Irish Sea, Tom was left on his own, as the rest of the convoy disappeared, but by keeping the sounding machine going he found he was in good depths of water, just about where he should be.

Early one morning when he should have been off the Skerries, Tom looked over his port side and saw one of the destroyers nearly alongside. It was dark and snowing, and the destroyer was showing dimmed navigation lights. Her Captain hailed Tom's ship and asked where the rest of the convoy was, and did Tom know his position? Tom answered him by saying he had not seen the other ships during the night, and he was about ten miles off the Skerries.

The destroyer left then to find the others, and by 8 a.m. Tom met up with the rest of the convoy, and steered a course for the Preston lightship, as he had not seen a thing since leaving Halifax. Only by keeping regular soundings could he judge where his approximate position was. Eight other ships trailed behind single line ahead, about two cables apart. Some of them were fairly big ships, with deep drafts. It was some forty miles to the Preston lightship, but on reaching that area he could not see it anywhere. The visibility was very poor, and it was becoming dark now, being a mid-winter night. Tom's officers stuck to the sounding machine, and were getting soundings every ten minutes, then they started to reduce in depth until he passed the ten-fathom line. He ran into seven fathoms just to make sure, then turned nearly ninety degrees to go south with the other ships following on. So they wound their way, keeping inside the ten fathoms. The leading destroyer came up and inquired about the manoeuvres. He said his sounding machine was out of order, taking it for granted that Tom knew where the ship was.

Sure enough, they picked up the Bar lightship ahead where the pilot would be obtained to take the ship up the river and into the dock. It was midnight when they picked up the pilot, and a very cold night it was too. On arriving at Gladstone Docks the ship was passed through, but the bridge over the locks into Hornby Docks was frozen and would not open. The ship could do nothing about this, so had to stay put until it was unfrozen.

Next morning she docked, and Tom was delighted when his wife and second son came down to meet him. At the Naval office he handed in his papers, and the two destroyer Captains made themselves known to Tom and congratulated him on his navigation the previous night.

The *Syrian Prince* did not stop long in Liverpool, soon off-loading the cargo of flour and foodstuffs. The chains and guns were for Devonport. So Tom did not have long with his wife and son.

She sailed for Devonport again and resumed her ammunition duties. A new crew was engaged, some of them never having been to sea before, but they were a fine set of men. All the officers, engineers included, had about seven days' leave, before she loaded ammunition and sailed for Halifax, Bermuda, and the West Indies, as before. But this time the *Syrian Prince* was to be away for two years.

Chapter 17

O N ARRIVING BACK IN HALIFAX, NOVA SCOTIA, the ship lay at the small jetty in Bedford Basin for about three weeks, with her load of ammunition, as she was a mobile ammunition supplier to ships at sea if necessary. Small craft could be supplied by coming alongside at the berth.

The ship had a lot of privileges in the supply of cigarettes and tobacco, smoking by the crew being confined however to their Mess, which was as far aft as possible. The Chief Petty Officer, RN, was acting Naval Supply Officer. He took the orders for stock, and saw to it that the right articles were delivered. The Marine sergeant kept the order book and made out receipts.

The *Syrian Prince* went to Bermuda in due course, and stayed there for some time, supplying HM cruisers when needed. Tom made friends with the dockyard Tugmaster, and found the association very instructive, with such incidents as the towing of a target for a warship to test its gunnery, when Tom always got an invitation to go with the tug. Warships would just come out of nowhere and let fly at the target, then be off again without making their number. Tom often thought one stray shot might hit the tug, and then what? It never happened, however, although one shell got caught in the lay of the wire tow rope.

It was an experience, too, when the tug was docking a ship, lying under the bow, pushing or pulling and seeming to make the ship tower above in a most menacing way. Tom considered this all good experience.

Sometimes he and the Chief Officer would rig up the ship's working boat and go for a sail to view shallow patches, where, looking down into the sea, all sorts of marine life could be seen and many attractive colours ornamented the view from different types of coral. Everything was so interesting that there was never a dull moment.

The Second Officer and the Marine bought themselves a 'Housey-Housey' outfit, so in the evenings nearly all the off-duty ratings of the dockyard sat around the after deck playing the game. Half the profits went to the sports fund of the ship.

The vessel would also visit Port Royal, Jamaica, where a certain amount of ammunition was landed in an old fort. A small new wooden jetty had been made about the length of the *Syrian Prince*, so she could tie up nicely there. Local labour was used for handling the munitions. The old dockyard was close by. It had been abandoned since the earthquake of the middle of the nineteenth century. This disturbance was said to have swallowed up half of the old town of Port Royal, and an old saying had it that one could hear the bell in the sunken church tolling when the sea was rough.

The dockyard followed the pattern of similar institutions in home waters and was as it stood in the time that Nelson had been stationed there as lieutenant. The buildings for officers' and mens' quarters had no roof on them, and iron hooks could be seen in the mess hall, in the overhead beams, for slinging their hammocks.

A clock was on the face of the officers' quarters, high up over the entrance, which was said to be over a hundred years old and was still going and keeping good time when Tom was there.

There was the Admiral's house where he and his lady no doubt ruled the dockyard society, and stretching up to this house was a tree-lined walk, where the same gentlemen would walk up and down, as men do when used to restricted spaces for exercise.

There was a perfectly built swimming pool, with a few old sheds, probably used as changing rooms for the bathers. The only thing wrong with the pool at the time Tom was there, was that the bottom was very muddy indeed, but one could swim without touching it.

Many old wooden stock anchors were lying around, and the timbers of the dockside were rotten. One would like to have had a glimpse into the high days of Port Royal and seen the activity of the dockyard, with the old-time sailing warships lying alongside. It would have been a very colourful scene. How an observer's imagination could be allowed to run riot in such surroundings on a calm, peaceful evening just after sundown.

Four Master Gunners and a Major were stationed just outside the dockyard, and Tom and his officers often visited their Mess. These men, with their families, were in charge of coloured troops. The Major was a middle-aged man, with a heavy moustache. He had risen from the ranks; in fact, he had served an apprenticeship at sea in sailing ships. His house was at the other end of the dockyard, where he lived with his wife and daughter, who was about eighteen years of age. They would visit the Mess in the evenings, and other Europeans, too, would visit this Mess, which provided the only social life to be had in that area.

Of course Tom and his officers were invited there, too, and one evening, just on the rise of a full moon, the Major's wife had come through the dockyard, making for this centre of social activity. She came into the Mess in a rather shaky condition, and after she had settled down somewhat she gave the company present this tale.

She was walking without any hurry through the dockyard, as she had done many times before, making for the gate to pass through from her residence to the Mess. Night falls quickly after sundown, but the full moon made more than sufficient light to see her on her way. Without much concern she saw a gentleman walking in front of her, his head bowed and his hands clasped behind his back as if he was in deep thought. Then it suddenly struck the Major's wife that he was dressed in the old-fashioned uniform of Nelson's period, cocked hat, blue coat, with large shoulder straps, white knickerbocker breeches and buckled shoes. She said she was not shocked or surprised at the sight of this venerable gentleman, as she felt he belonged to the place and had more right to be there than she had. But what did startle her was that as they approached the door at that end of the dockyard he gradually melted into nothing and was nowhere to be seen.

All listened with great interest. This was no joke, it was a fact. Perhaps the surroundings made the supernatural appear more real to them and acted on their imagination, but who knows the truth of such things?

One of the Master Gunners had a story to confirm such a tale. While lying, in bed with his rather oversized dog sleeping on the floor of his room, he put a hand up to switch off the light and noticed the dog with all his hair standing on end, eyes glassy with apprehension. Something then gripped his wrist with an ice-cold clasp and held it suspended. How long this state of affairs lasted he could not say, but it was long enough to realise how real the whole incident was, though it may have been only seconds. Perhaps some uneasy soul of the past was still roaming around looking for a resting place.

Not far from the dockyard were the remains of an old fort. Indeed, it was not the only one, but this one had a particular interest. It was in a good state of preservation, and was built in the form of a square, with very thick walls reaching to about fifteen feet high. These walls were terraced every five feet with a flat base about six feet wide, no doubt in order to have guns at that level on each platform. Openings were in the walls for such artillery.

These walls encompassed about a thousand square feet of ground. On the second terrace level was a door which led into a room built into the wall, and on this door was inscribed the name, Lieut H. Nelson. On the side of the wall was a notice reading, 'He who walks here tread lightly, as Lieut Nelson walked here.'

The gate of this fort, or the opening for the gate, had at the foot of each side large fender stones to prevent carriage wheels damaging the wall. Near sundown, when shadows were lengthening, they looked like three women sitting at the gate, in the robes of those days, with bowed heads. These were supposed to be Nelson's three mistresses who are believed to be buried just outside the gate. Nelson must have been quite a boy.

Much of the ammunition was landed into one of the forts for the warships then on station. The fort was thoroughly cleaned out of weeds and rubbish, then all the stonework whitewashed. The *Syrian Prince* always kept enough on board for any emergency. Working in these surroundings, though, set one's mind back to other colourful days of strife. Abandoned old guns were just lying about anywhere; in fact, the bollards on the wooden jetty were up-ended old muzzle loader guns. It was noticed by Tom that none of these articles of war had any sign of rust.

The *Syrian Prince* had bunkered with coal at Bermuda before coming down to Jamaica. This coal which was stacked in the dockyard must have been swarming with rats, and Tom's Chief Officer, a little Welshman and an excellent officer, set large wire cage traps to try to catch them. He made a good job of this, but still one or two were about. They were big devils, and they could be heard squealing during the nights.

Tom was lying on the top of his bed one night, in the buff as the weather was tropical, when he was awakened by a soft touch on his chest. When he had gathered his senses, he called the Second Officer who was on watch, and they searched Tom's room for the intruder. Sure enough, there was a huge rat clinging to the pipe under the bath.

They each found a sizeable piece of wood, blocked off all openings out of the bathroom and then got busy. The thing was jumping about all over the place, but they finished it off after half an hour's battle. It was a great black rat, and it nearly made both of them sick to look at it. It must have been in Tom's bed when he turned in that night.

Eventually they were all trapped and put an end to. The ship could do nicely without such company.

They went to Trinidad next, a very nice place, and Tom had made many friends there. The Harbourmaster came from South Shields, as also did his wife. He had been a diver on the building of the port, which was practically new, and they always gave the Chief Engineer and Tom a great welcome.

Some ammunition had to be landed here. This was in the care of the Ammunition Supply Officer from Bermuda, who was travelling with the ship, and local labour was used. An old sugar warehouse was loaned to them for this purpose somewhere outside the port area, but after it had been cleaned out and the ammunition transferred, the bottom of the warehouse gave way, and the ammo dropped through on to a syrupy mixture below, so it all had to be re-stowed somewhere else.

After Trinidad the ship went back to Bermuda for a while, and then to Halifax. When they received orders to go to Halifax most of the British people in the dockyard would give Tom mail orders for clothing. They would take the number of the article from the mail order book, fill in their forms, and on arrival at Halifax he would present them to the store of the mail order book, give a date for delivery and pay for the orders. Soon a van would come down with a host of parcels with the names of those on the order forms clearly marked. On arrival at Bermuda the goods were taken by the dockyard for delivery to their owners. Gifts of fish were also taken from Halifax Dockyard to Bermuda Dockyard; no money transaction whatsoever.

While here the ship took on more ammo from the UK which came out by ship, instead of the *Syrian Prince* having to go to Devonport for it. The submarine war was hotting up somewhat by now. As she had freezer space, stores were carried in there for the dockyard Naval staff from the Halifax dockyard, plenty of nice big codfish, lobsters and other food which could not be got in Bermuda. When Tom arrived at Bermuda from the north he was like Father Christmas to all. Cigarettes, too, were obtained for the Messes.

After about a year of this business, and the ship being in Bermuda, orders came from the Home Admiralty to off-load all the ammo and go to Freetown, West Africa. Tom got permission to bunker at Trinidad and off they went.

On arriving at Trinidad the ship was taken alongside under the coal apparatus. After arriving there, they found that it was the last day and night of Mardi Gras celebrations, and the Harbourmaster informed Tom he would not be ready to sail until early morning. So Tom and the Chief Engineer got all dolled up and went to see the celebrations.

They were introduced to the local Mayor and all the top folks. It was the final dancing period, which was held in the Mayor's own extensive grounds, surrounded by fruit trees and highly perfumed flowers. Tables were laid out with all kinds of exotic foods, platters, punch and bottles of well-known brands. The music was playing, and all were enjoying themselves. The Chief and Tom often visited the tables for a little nourishment, which kept them both happy, but next morning at 4 a.m. they came back to the ship still as sober as judges.

Chapter 18

Two hours later the *Syrian Prince* left for Freetown, Sierra Leone. The instructions for routing were given by Naval Control. Arriving at Freetown she was put alongside the ammunition ship stationed there, which happened to be a ship fitting out at Devonport while the *Syrian Prince* was doing the same. Apparently she was being relieved from this station because she was unsuitable for the tropical climate.

She was one of the Cork Steamship Company's ships, and had only been used for coastal work from Manchester to the Continent before being taken over. She had been lying at Freetown since October 1939, and now it was March 1941. The barnacles on the ship's bottom were standing out about three feet all round and underneath.

When all the ammo had been transferred, the *Syrian Prince* was left to carry on with the work. Somewhere about this time the through passage of the Mediterranean Sea was closed to shipping. This meant that all convoys bound for Suez or further east had to go around the Cape of Good Hope, South Africa, and Freetown was used as a halfway house for bunkers of oil and coal, and fresh water. Two ships were there with special machinery in their holds to make fresh water from sea water.

The escorts, corvettes and destroyers came alongside the *Syrian Prince* for replenishments of ammunition, etc. Often their forty-ton refrigerator space contained foodstuffs from the store ship for distribution to the small warships.

The *Syrian Prince* lay in Freetown until May 1942, during which time Tom was engaged in piloting ships into the anchorage, assisted by about a dozen Royal Naval Reserve officers. An average convoy was about seventy-five ships, which all had to be inside the boom defence by nightfall, on account of the German U-boats being around in great numbers. They would sink any ship left outside at night-time.

Tom never had any time to get bored as he was on the move all the while. Also, he realised he was gaining a tremendous amount of experience in handling ships of all sizes, as every one was much bigger than the *Syrian Prince*. The troop convoys were ex-passenger liners, and he had them all.

One of the Union Castle ships was base ship, on which there was a hospital, also recreation and rest rooms for the men on the small warships.

The ship was the *Edinburgh Castle*, and Tom, with his deck and engineer officers, generally went over to her on a Sunday evening to have a meal and see a movie, and have a chat with some of the Naval officers they had got to know.

In course of time the *Syrian Prince* was beginning to be too small to take all the shipments of ammo from the UK. The bins were being overstowed to carry all that was needed, which meant moving stuff about to get at any particular type of ammo needed. Time was being wasted on deliveries, and a bigger ship was needed.

One day a French ship was captured, with a full load of native troops. The French had taken one or two British ships into captivity. She was brought into Freetown and it was suggested that she could be fitted out for ammunition. She was about eight thousand tons deadweight, but when she was inspected by the Naval people she was in a filthy condition. It was decided to send her to Cape Town to be fitted out, and she was put into the care of Elder Dempster's shipping company.

She was away about five months before the fitting out was completed. When she returned Tom tied up the *Syrian Prince* alongside her, and the ammunition and stock was discharged into the French ship, which had plenty of room.

Now the *Syrian Prince* was ordered to Lagos for dry-docking, and it was unbelievable the amount of sea growth that had collected on the bottom. Her average speed was twelve knots when clean, but on the way to Lagos she could only do five knots, and so could not keep up with the convoy. Tom edged her over to the coast, and so arrived at Lagos in good shape, while some of the ships in the convoy were sunk by U-Boats.

The floating dock could just take the *Syrian Prince* so the bottom was cleaned by native labour, and when she was ready they went up to Accra, on the Gold Coast, to load a full cargo of peanuts.

This cargo was for Liverpool, and after she was loaded, Tom had to go into Freetown again to join a convoy going to the UK.

The usual practice, when a convoy was expected very early in the morning, was that a boat would come to the ship to pick Tom up about four o'clock. There were four base ships — two oilers, one store ship and themselves. Off they would go to a Dutch tug, the *Nord Zee*, where the RNR pilots were. They would go well out to sea in the tug with two fast motor launches alongside. When the ships were seen approaching in two columns they took to the motor launches, six in each. One boat went to each column, which put them on the pilot ladder, then shoved off to the next one. Tom was once left dangling in mid-air on the pilot ladder as the crew had put it over the bow. He had a few words to say to the officer in charge of that outfit! They would run each ship over the de-gaussing range, then into the anchorage as instructed on a plan provided by the Naval authorities. As soon as the anchor was down and the boats back, they were picked up again and repeated the performance. Freetown was the half-way port for the ships going around the Cape to Egypt and India. They would then be routed for the rest of the way.

The *Edinburgh Castle* was the base ship in port. She flew the White Ensign, and being an old passenger ship she had plenty of accommodation for men on base duties, also a hospital. Movies would be exhibited twice a week on Wednesday and Sunday evenings. Most of the crew generally did the Sunday show, having their own motor boat for transport.

The *Oxfordshire* was the hospital ship; she had doctors and nurses, and plenty of facilities for the sick. Malaria was common – nearly all the crew had it in varying degrees, except the Chief Engineer and Tom. The taking of anti-malaria tablets was compulsory for everyone. Whenever possible the football team was away ashore, or as many as they could safely send for a kick about or a match with other ships. The chief and Tom would sometimes be asked to dinner at the Naval mess and play bridge in the slack periods. It all helped to keep them fit and occupied.

When enough ships had been collected the Masters attended a convoy conference as usual in Admiralty House ashore to get all the information from the Commodore about position in convoy and a host of other instructions should the convoy be attacked. The Masters were so accustomed to convoy drill that it came as second nature to them.

They had one old destroyer and a US Coastguard ship as escort. They sailed after the conference, and soon were in line abreast and single line ahead steaming at seven and a half knots.

They arrived safe enough at Liverpool in June 1942, where Tom's wife and youngest son came down. Having been away from home for over two years everybody was due for leave. When paid off they all left the ship and a new Master and crew took her over.

Tom had been home about one month when he was called upon to go to Southampton to relieve a Master on the small *Arabian Prince* similar to the *Syrian Prince*. He took her to Cardiff in a coastal convoy and then came back home again.

During his home leave he was glad to be with his wife and sons again, and realised how much he had missed in the way of family life. During the time he had been away his home had had the roof blown off by a land mine dropped by enemy aircraft. Fortunately his wife and children were in the air raid shelter in the back garden. It must have been a terrible experience for them. Most of the furniture was a write-off as it was so damaged, and Tom could imagine how his wife must have felt, having no one to help her. Indeed, Tom did not know just what had happened, as all mail had to go through the GPO in London, and the only letter he did get was to say that she and the boys had moved to near the coast.

The folks at home were as much in the active war as the men who were away, engaged in it. Fortunately, Tom's sons were able to attend a private school in the new town of residence. This school did not evacuate to the country, as it had its own crypt in which the scholars could lie low in the event of air raids.

Chapter 19

Tom was not at home very long before he had to go to Liverpool to relieve the Master on the *Tudor Prince*. When he arrived on board he found that this Master had had a very tough passage across, for the convoy had been attacked by enemy submarines and several ships were sunk. This man's nerve had gone, and he was a hospital case. This meant that Tom had to take the ship for the next voyage to Halifax, Nova Scotia, and back to Liverpool. In those days one could not very well refuse, so he had himself put on the Ship's Register at the Customs House. The ship was about a thousand tons bigger than the *Syrian Prince*. Tom had had enough of the small ships, and this was one. He took the ship for one voyage only, after which possibly the other Master would be ready for sea again.

When she was ready for sea Tom went to the convoy conference with other Masters. It was like meeting old friends again. The usual business was attended to and each Master left for his ship with his attaché case full of papers relating to the convoy. These had to be sunk at sea if the ship was sunk or badly damaged, so as not to fall into the enemy's hands. A special weighted bag was used to keep the documents in, which could easily be disposed of. When the ship arrived safely the papers were handed over to Naval Control.

Another device which had been fitted on all ships was the fog buoy. This was attached to a thin wire rope on a small winch of its own. In fog, and there was plenty of that on the North Atlantic crossing, this fog buoy was put over the stern and streamed for two cables, which is twelve hundred feet. The buoy was so made that it scooped the water up and discharged it through a small pipe on top of the float, through the action of being towed. Thereby, in a thick fog, when ships could not see each other, they could keep station by keeping this fog buoy on the beam. Each ship streamed one of these devices except the last ones in line. The jet of water the buoy shot up in the air, about two or three feet, could be seen or even heard in the darkness of the night.

The voyage was not so bad outward, and on arriving at Halifax ammunition was discharged at Bedford Basin, then she went over to the town docks. Tom met many friends of his *Syrian Prince* days in the course of his duties.

The *Tudor Prince* was loaded with a cargo of foodstuffs down in some of the holds along with other goods, also a considerable amount of something new in high explosives for filling depth charges. Strange to say, Tom met the American Captain of an oil tanker whom he had met previously in Halifax in the very early part of the war. He was sailing in the same convoy homewards.

At the conference Tom found he was right behind his American friend's tanker in the second column. He was Number Three and Tom was Number Four. He had told Tom his ship was loaded with aviation spirit.

The ships left as usual, single line ahead until outside, and then they formed up, with a Blue Funnel ship as Commodore. This was October 1942, and the U-Boats were then working in packs of about five. The submarine war was at its height, but there was a serious shortage of escorts. After the Canadian destroyers left, off Newfoundland, only two United States small craft were the escorts. Tom would not call them destroyers, as they were too small to be in that class. This was the first time US ships had been on escort duty.

The convoy proceeded on its way, but about halfway across it was attacked, several ships being hit at different positions in the convoy. This was after dark, and the Commodore was giving the signal for emergency course alterations. Then at midnight Tom's friend in the tanker ahead got it, and in seconds she was ablaze; the heat was tremendous. Tom had to get out of her way, but with the convoy speed being only seven and a half knots the fires down in the boiler room were low.

SS *Tudor Prince.*

Tom was thinking of the explosives down the hold. He rang the engine room to give the speed, as the ship could not answer her helm quickly enough to avoid her going into the flames of the ship ahead. But slowly she came round, just skimming the edge of the flaming mass on the water.

At the same time he had to avoid running into the next column of ships, which would cause considerable confusion. At last he got past the ship, which could not be seen for flames and smoke. Tom thought, 'There goes my old friend along with his crew,' for from what he saw he could not understand anyone coming out alive. In all probability it would be sudden death for all, but to Tom's amazement, as she passed close to his ship, she had three or four survivors on deck.

A ship which was behind the *Tudor Prince* must have dropped astern. Tom knew she had the same type of cargo as his own ship, as she had been loading in the next berth to him in Halifax. He soon knew where she was, as a terrific explosion was heard astern of the convoy. She had been torpedoed, and he could not imagine any lives being saved.

Tom got himself back into station, and in the morning he could see the empty spaces in the lines and gathered that about five ships had been sunk.

That very night came a second attack. It must have been between ten and eleven p.m. Abreast of the *Tudor Prince* was a large whale oil ship on the port side, about three cables distance. Tom was sitting in his armchair in the wheelhouse, having a cat-nap, when there came the noise of a torpedo exploding. So close was the noise that he thought it was his ship, but it was the whale oil ship. Her bow must have gone down about twelve feet and she remained so. Those whale oil ships had many compartments and many oil-tight bulkheads, so she remained afloat. The torpedo must have hit her well forward. She was able to carry on, as no doubt the Captain did not want to linger there and be a sitting target. He would know his ship, and the possibility of keeping afloat.

Again on the port side of the *Tudor Prince* another ship got it. She soon sank, but many survivors were taken on to the escort. Where they put the men, the Lord only knows: probably on to some ship in the convoy, which was making emergency turns to avoid being hit by other torpedoes. Tom thought that if that torpedo had missed the whaler it would have blown the little *Tudor Prince* sky-high. Seven ships were lost in the convoy altogether.

They proceeded on a pre-arranged zig-zag course, which was the only way to prevent exposing a ship for any length of time as a target for a U-Boat, for although a stray shot might find a home in one of the ships, the action taken reduced the possibility of a direct hit in a vital part.

As far as Tom can remember, the submarine attacks must have taken place about the twentieth meridian and sixty degrees north. The sea was rough, and it was very black at night. The next day, however, the Home escort of three business-like destroyers took over and were buzzing around all the time, dropping depth charges. They actually replenished their bunker fuel from one of the tankers.

Tom and his officers were on the alert all the time for sighting submarine periscopes and keeping their station in the convoy.

Eventually they arrived in UK waters via Northern Ireland. Glasgow ships went their way, and the Liverpool ships likewise. When the *Tudor Prince* arrived in the Liverpool docks Air Force officers boarded her and questioned Tom about the attack, asking whether any 'planes had been seen, but during the night nothing much could be observed, only the results of direct hits by torpedoes.

Liverpool had had its share of air attacks, which had caused havoc in the docks.

After the tension endured on the passage across Tom found it difficult at first to relax, but fixing up the men's pay sheets and paying off the ship was something to take his mind off it all, and he got back to normal routine.

Chapter 20

THE SUPERINTENDENT CAME ON BOARD to inform Tom that he was to be transferred to the *Indian Prince*, which was loading not far away, for the North African campaign. Tom went over to her and found that she was a much larger ship, about eleven thousand tons deadweight, one of the Far Eastern ships. She had twin screws, with two motor engines, and her normal speed was about fifteen knots.

This ship was loading in Gladstone docks with war material for North Africa, as well as with many bags of mail. When she had completed loading in the holds, number one hold was loaded with cans of aviation spirit, with special vents up the foremast to clear the gas from the hold.

Two large RAF rescue launches were loaded on deck, one forward and one aft. These launches were stowed athwartships, resting on the gunwales. The ship had a beam measurement of sixty feet, and these boats were protruding about six feet over each side. Of course they were well secured. This meant the ship could only go through the locks on the top of high water, so that the overhang of the boats could clear the locks. She got out into the river all right, and anchored there along with other ships going out in the convoy.

Tom and the other Masters had to come back on shore by tug boat to the conference at Naval Control. On arriving there they were given the usual lecture and position in the convoy. The main convoy was made up off the Tail of the Bank in the River Clyde. They would be met off Northern Ireland, where the convoy would form up. They came back to their ships with the usual bag of secret papers on convoy instructions. They were bound for Algiers.

They met the other convoy as instructed, and took their numbered place. This convoy, of about sixty ships, was very well protected, with one cruiser and six destroyers. The latter were cruising well out ahead, astern and abeam. The cruiser was anti-aircraft.

The convoy sailed without much further ado, steaming out to about fifteen degrees west and so down south. In course of time she passed through the Straits of Gibraltar, and so to Algiers. Coming through the Straits all ships were in single line, with their paravanes out to throw moored mines clear, if any. Spanish and Moroccan fishermen were near, they were at liberty to inform all and sundry that the convoy had gone through.

The *Indian Prince* had to go into port first, as she had the mail. She went in and tied up to the quayside, and commenced work with local stevedores. This was late in November 1942, and after discharging she went home again by convoy. Ships lying out in the Bay could be blown up by mines planted there by enemy swimmers, and one or two ships got this treatment while waiting to berth. Where the planters of these mines to the underwater parts of the ship worked from was unknown.

The *Indian Prince* went in a convoy of about thirty ships, with a couple of escorts and a fast specialised ship for mine-laying. The speed was seven and a half knots, zig-zagging after clearing the Spanish coast. When approaching the Irish coast the faster ships such as the *Indian Prince* were allowed to go full speed to their destination under the care of the fast minelayer. This was to avoid confusion at Liverpool with too many ships arriving at one time.

Coming up the west Irish coast, Tom checked his position by soundings and found the convoy was too far towards land. He informed the HM ship, but he kept on. He saw trouble ahead off the Shannon, as rocks and all kinds of islands were well out to sea. He hauled out, informing the HM ship, and picked up the convoy again at Tory Island. He heard later that a brand-new ship in the convoy had piled up on a rock, and all had to make an emergency turn to clear.

The *Indian Prince* went to Birkenhead, this time, to load, and Tom's wife and two of his sons came down to be with him while in port. It was not much pleasure for them in war-time, but they belonged to each other and that was enough for them.

The ship loaded again for North Africa, this being in January 1943. It took about fourteen days to load and this was a rare mixture of a cargo of war implements and ammo, with number one hold filled with flimsy cans of aviation spirit.

It was at this port, while signing on a new crew at the shipping office, that the Mercantile Marine Superintendent asked Captain Sloane and all his officers and men if they would be willing to take part in the invasion of France, when that operation went into force. All agreed, and so had their identity cards stamped with the letter 'V'.

When the ship was loaded, Tom's wife and sons went home, as he had many things to do, such as the usual conference and the ship to be taken out to anchor. On the way down through the docks to the river locks, however, something went wrong with the engines, and she was held up for a day, which was making her late for the convoy. She eventually sailed the next evening, but the fog had come down and was so thick that the pilot would not take the ship into the river. There were none of the usual aids to navigation one sees today. Off Seaforth, if the exact position was in doubt, as in fog, the ship could easily finish up half in and half ashore on what is called the wall, on the north side of the channel. That would mean her back would be broken in no time. Tom had seen a passenger ship in this predicament, her stern in deep water and her bow on the wall. The wall cannot be seen as it is below water level. It is there so that the channel will not silt up.

Next forenoon she finally sailed, but for the Tail of the Bank, off Gourock, at the entrance to the river Clyde. The convoy had left two days before, and the *Indian Prince* had now to wait about ten days for the next one.

When all ships had gathered at the Tail of the Bank the time came to attend the convoy conference. There were about one hundred and fifty ships at anchor between Loch Long and the Gairloch, which comprised three convoys going different ways.

Motor boats came off to the ships for the North African convoy and took the Masters and the Wireless Officers this time ashore to Gourock. A Naval Captain was in the chair and about six destroyer Captains, with all the Shipmasters sitting around the table in mufti as usual. By this time all the Masters knew each other, as they had attended so many of these conferences. The Wireless Officers were taken to another room where they were on the messages procedure.

When the conference was over they were told that the convoy would leave at 6.00 next morning, single line, with the Commodore, who was RN, in the leading ship. His ship would heave up first and leave, followed by the rest of the ships in turn as designated, so that there would be no confusion.

The conference ended about 5 p.m. and all Masters were told to go back to their ships as soon as possible, and get them ready immediately, as a severe storm was expected over the area that night.

As the *Indian Prince* was a motor ship, that was soon done when Tom arrived back and gave the orders. About 10 p.m. the wind was gale force and increasing to severe gale, and Tom was on the navigating bridge watching for any dragging of the anchor, as he had sixty fathoms of chain out on the starboard anchor.

In the black darkness he could not see very far, but the storm was taking its toll on some of the ships. He could see the two red lights going up; these in a vertical line, one above the other and not less than six feet apart, are the signal for a ship aground or disabled, and not under command. Ships were dragging and going ashore, and others colliding with each other.

Tom saw two ships, locked together, bearing down on top of him. Shortly one was across the bow and the other alongside, and he had the cable slacked away to ease the impact. The *Indian Prince* boats were not swung out yet, as usual when going to sea, but the other ship's boats were, and they were caught on the fish plate on the boat deck, severely damaging the boats on the starboard side.

Tom yelled, 'Have you got no steam?' and the other ship's Captain came back with the answer that he had no steam up and was helpless. This other ship was beginning to pound the bow, which alarmed Tom on account of the high octane spirit in number one hold. If the other ship holed the bow the whole lot was liable to catch fire from the sparks of steel plates rubbing against each other.

Captain Tom Sloane decided to get out of this situation as quickly as possible. There were ships all round him, but he was going to get out of this hole. He had the cable hove in slowly and dead slow ahead on the engines, and was pleased to see the two ships slipping back. The one on the bow was pressing heavily on to the port side bulwarks. The gale was then about force ten, which meant that when the anchor came off the bottom he had to watch himself, as these other two would carry him with them for the shore, which was not far off. So he pushed the ship ahead at half speed, just clearing another ship at anchor, then the other two slipped off, bearing for the shore.

As all ships at anchor would now be stretching their cables tight with the weight of the storm, and have the limit out, Tom had to be careful that he did not run over such anchor chains, as they would tear the bottom plates out of the *Indian Prince*.

Well, he got away, and anchored his ship just off the Holy Loch, clear of the ships. Many had gone ashore, and the warning red lights were numerous. One ship was nearly cut in two by another ship's bow, and over the side Tom could see the great gash.

He and his officers examined the damage to the *Indian Prince*, and found the port side bulwarks, forward, bent and buckled. The steel deck was also severely buckled. The boats were all right as the other ship had only damaged her own.

The whole matter was reported to the Naval officer in charge. The buckled plates were tested for water tightness, with a good pressure of water through the fire hose, and they were found tight enough.

It was now the small hours of the morning, so Tom had a cat-nap in his chair. When it came to their turn to heave up next morning the anchor chain came up, but no anchor. The anchor pin must have worked loose and come out as the anchor was being lifted. The ship could not stop for that, but when passing the signal station the matter was reported to the Naval officer.

SS Indian Prince.

Some of the convoy came up from Liverpool and South Wales, so it was a fairly big convoy. Six destroyers were their escorts, with one submarine. They soon formed up and made their way south. Orders were received, on passing Gibraltar, for the *Indian Prince* to proceed to Bone. Bone was close to where the new army of British and US forces was attacking from the west. Four ships were taking their cargoes to that port, the *Indian Prince* included. They went along the North African coast in single line, and on arriving there the ships were taken into port by French pilots. The Army Pioneer Corps were discharging the cargo.

They duly arrived at port and came into the little harbour and alongside the wharf. The Pioneer Corps of the Army did the discharging, working day and night. Every night at dusk the German dive bombers made an attack on the harbour, zooming about all over the place, bombing and machine-gunning. The soldiers would leave the ship in an orderly manner immediately on the commencement of the raids. Smoke screens were set off to cover the whole harbour. By jove, that was the stuff to make one cough and sneeze. The warships in port (cruisers) would blast away – one could hear the orders being issued to their guns. The guns on the *Indian Prince* too fired away, together with all the merchant ships until the all-clear went. Their ship was armed with one 4.7 on the stern, twelve oerlikons, six a side and twenty-four rockets on the boat deck. They had an Army gun crew of ten men, also a Naval crew of three men, the rest of the gun's crew being made up of their own men, and everyone was engaged.

A RNR Commander came on board and introduced himself as being in charge of the shipping, and as soon as Tom heard him talking he knew he was from his part of the world. He was from Tynemouth, and they soon became friends.

There were two cruisers stationed here, HMS *Dido* being one of them. These ships raided the Italian and German ships crossing over to Rommel's army with troops and supplies. In the end they blocked off all connections with Italy for the German and Italian Forces. Although conditions were pretty good during the day, at night the harbour was attacked by enemy dive bombers.

The Pioneers would work right up to the last minute, then leave the ship in an orderly manner. Smoke screens would be set off all around on the hills and harbour, which completely covered all in black smoke, making everybody cough.

All the guns were manned on the ship, the same as all the others. The cruisers were so close that one could hear the officer talking, giving the positions of the attacking force of 'planes, then giving instructions to the guns in a very matter of fact voice. The guns on the warships moved as easily as one's own fingers.

The *Indian Prince* was well armed. The gunnery officer was the Second Officer. The Chief Officer had charge of the fire-fighting gang, and the Third Officer was the Captain's right-hand man when in action. The ship herself could be called a fairly big one for her day.

One night a dive bomber dived right into the water, probably brought down by gunfire. Every night this performance would go on for two or three hours, then be quiet again until the next night. Probably the Germans were running short of bombs. Strange to say, the only ship to be hit was an oil tanker, which immediately caught fire. All the ammunition and high octane spirit was stacked on the quay from the *Indian Prince*, and trucks were taking it away as fast as they could.

As all the Army and Navy personnel were eating out of tins, it was suggested by Tom's friend, the Commander, that he could bring a little food up to his temporary lodgings and they could make a night of it. This was done, and along went Tom with the Chief Engineer loaded up with chickens and vegetables of all sorts. The lady of the house cooked the food, and she sat down with them. Maybe it had been a long time since she had seen a good meal. So with a couple of bottles of wine, all enjoyed the meal while things were quiet.

Tom had mentioned to the Commander that he had lost an anchor on leaving the Clyde. Two or three days afterwards there was an anchor alongside in a barge, with fifteen fathoms of chain. It came out of a wreck, and was about the size the ship needed, so Tom took it, two anchors being better than one.

When the four ships had discharged their cargo they left for Algiers to join up with a convoy leaving there. With the convoy they left for the UK. The *Indian Prince* had to go to Cardiff this time to load. She was about four weeks there, loading ammunition and supplies for the Middle East, but as there was no passage through the Mediterranean she would have to go around the Cape of Good Hope.

Tom's wife came down to the ship during the loading period, so they had three good weeks together.

Eventually the ship completed loading, and now she had to go to Milford Haven to anchor there until all ships had collected from this area. Ships would be leaving Liverpool and the Tail of the Bank, and all would form up in the convoy off Northern Ireland. The Masters received their instructions and their number in the final set-up. Captain Tom Sloane was appointed Commodore on the *Indian Prince*. She had to go first and the others came behind in single line, with an escort of one destroyer.

They passed the Smalls lighthouse, three miles off, and proceeded up the Irish Sea, on a direct course to the Isle of Man, where they would meet the Liverpool ships, forming two columns with them and so to the North of Ireland, where they met up with the Clyde section, which carried the RN Commodore. At a given signal each ship took its allotted station, taking particular notice of the column they were to be in and the number of the ship which would be in front of them. The Clyde ships took the head of their columns, and the others had to come up from behind to take their place.

When the convoy was formed up all moved forward at seven and a half knots. They were well protected by six destroyers, who were cruising about on all quarters of the compass. This convoy was bound for the southern tip of South Africa, to round the Cape and come up the east coast of Africa to Suez Bay.

When about abreast of Gibraltar a destroyer came up and hailed the ship, saying that they were to proceed direct to Gibraltar. Tom saw three other ships breaking out of the convoy, and they proceeded at full speed to Gibraltar and arrived there next day.

The Masters were taken ashore by launch to attend a conference where they were told they would be proceeding through the Mediterranean to Port Said. They formed up and carried on through with a heavy escort, four destroyers and an anti-aircraft cruiser, anchoring at Bone first to wait for the mine-sweepers. The Gulf of Tunis and Cape Bone area were heavily mined by the enemy.

The mine-sweepers swept a channel and dropped Dan buoys to mark this channel while the ships came through in single line at slow speed.

Mines were bobbing up to the right and left of the ships, and the gunners had a few shots at them with oerlikon guns to try to explode or sink them. Many were hit, but nothing spectacular happened; they would apparently be harmless when full of water and sunk.

After passing Cape Bone the ships made for Tobruk and so picked up another convoy going east. Rather surprisingly no attack occurred, and the *Indian Prince* arrived safely at Port Said, and so went through the Canal to Suez Bay. Many troopers were there, practising landing troops on the beaches for the invasion of Italy. Apparently the cargoes of the four ships were needed urgently.

After discharging all the cargo the *Indian Prince* proceeded to Aden. It seemed strange to Tom to be around this area again.

Arriving there he received orders to proceed to Tamatave, on the east coast of Madagascar, to load produce of the island: ground nuts, coffee and tea. This produce had been in store for a long time, there being no ships to take it away. They were well treated by the French people, and when the ship had taken all there was to take she went to Mananjary, a few miles to the south, anchored there and loaded more cargo from lighters. The French people at this place, too, were very hospitable.

The ship was provided with fresh beef and many wild ducks, and other food necessary for the crew. It was a standing order to store up abroad when possible to save taking food out of Britain. Tom and the Chief Steward were entertained to a splendid meal by the chief Frenchman at that port, if it could be called a port, being a small bay used as a hot weather retreat by Europeans out there engaged in farming.

A British missionary and his wife and little girl joined the ship there for a passage over to Beira. He was going to Rhodesia for a holiday, after spending about twelve years in Madagascar in charge of the British Foreign Bible Society's business there. All seemed to go well on this passage, and the ship in due course arrived at Beira in Portuguese East Africa.

The ship loaded copper at this port, and was nearly full of cargo and down to her marks. From here she proceeded to Port Sudan, in the Red Sea, to load baled cotton. Now she was loading down the extra few inches which was allowed during the war to take all cargo possible.

The ship was now homeward bound through the Suez Canal and the Mediterranean. This sea was free for passage, but in convoy.

This was September 1943, and the *Indian Prince* was bound for Liverpool. On the way she had some engine trouble, and went into Malta, which was well battered by the air raids, and Tom was taken round to see the damage. Over at the dockyard area all buildings were a mess of rubble, but standing up in the middle of this rubble was a statue of the Holy Mother, Mary, with the Christ Child in her arms, practically untouched. The Maltese people considered this a miracle, and treated the statue as a real holy shrine, which in the time of the heavy air raids gave them great hope for the future.

The company agents there had very little food, and Tom was able to provide them with some. In forty-eight hours the ship left in the next convoy, and proceeded to Gibraltar.

At Gib. a convoy was made up again and they went on to Liverpool. On arrival the discharging of the cargo was commenced immediately, while Tom was engaged in paying off his crew and squaring up accounts for his employers for the voyage, which took about three days. After that he went home until the cargo was all discharged, as she had to go across the river to Birkenhead to load with war material, for Bombay this time.

The Bibby Line were acting as agents for this cargo, and the Superintendent of that line brought the proposed stowage plan for the cargo, which had come from the Ministry of Shipping in London. The Chief Officer and Tom worked out the stability and trim by this plan and found the ship would be down by the head when finished, so adjustments were made before loading began, which worked out as required.

Tom's wife was aboard with two of his sons, so they made the most of their stay in Birkenhead Docks. The ship took about fourteen days to load, working day and night. Most of the cargo was high explosive ammunition. As an 11,000-ton ship she took plenty, and loaded mostly ICI products. On the peace-time Far East trade she loaded latex in bulk, coconut oil and palm oil in those tanks.

The time came to sail again, and Tom's wife and sons went home again to Tynemouth. The crew was signed on, and all was ready for sailing, so up to the Tail of the Bank she went to join the convoy. The conference was attended, with the usual instructions. The convoy was for Mediterranean ports, and ships going to India, to Port Said and the Suez Canal for transit.

By now the Italian Army and Navy had capitulated. Sicily had been taken by the Allied Forces, and they were knocking at the door of Italy itself. But the Germans were fighting back hard.

The convoy proceeded towards Gibraltar. Plenty of escorts were now available, as many had been built during the last twelve months, especially of the corvette class.

The time of sailing from the UK was at the beginning of November 1943. Coming through the Straits of Gibraltar, all ships in single line, it must have looked never-ending to the local fishermen on both sides of the Straits. No doubt this information would be given to enemy sources. The convoy formed up again after passing into the Mediterranean.

The *Indian Prince* was the second ship in the third column, counting from the left, with about seventy ships in the convoy. It was 11 November when the ships for Oran broke away and made for that port. The convoy was now moving towards Algiers. Just before sundown the signal was passed down the convoy that an attack by air could be expected that night. Tom was just having his evening meal at 7.00 when shots were heard, so up to the bridge he ran, and the signal was given for action stations.

Oerlican guns were firing from the ships, and coloured tracer bullets could be seen on the right side of the convoy. A huge black 'plane was right ahead of the *Indian Prince*, coming towards her. Terrific explosions were heard and seen as ships were blowing up. All the guns of the *Indian Prince* were firing into the 'plane as it roared over. Several could now be seen, looking like huge bats in the sky. It was remarkable how one could imagine shapes of things in the height of battle.

These 'planes were dropping homing torpedoes. The 'bats' were falling out of the sky, and ships were being blown up. The gunners poured shells and tracer bullets into the 'bats', and the one roaring over the *Indian Prince* flopped into the sea, but just then a terrific explosion happened just forward of the bridge. The ship had received one amidships, and great clouds of smoke were coming out of the ventilators. Soon they knew that the *Indian Prince*'s back was broken.

Captain Tom Sloane was on the bridge, with both hands on the front teak rail. The signal halyards from the signal yard on the foremast were made fast just where he was standing. They tightened over his hands as the foremast leaned forward and with difficulty he pulled them free. The steering wheel had come off, and the helmsman was holding it in his hand. The Chief Officer, standing by with hoses at the ready, pulled the emergency stops, shutting off the supply of oil to the engines.

The engines were stopped, not by the action of the Chief Officer but by the Chief Engineer down in the engine room. With his crew they bolted up the ladder and saw the engine room bulkhead giving way under the weight of the sea water on the other side.

The engine room was filled in no time, but the Chief and his men had got out. She had been hit in the deep tanks, the only place where there was no explosive cargo. As the ship was sinking slowly, Captain Tom ordered all hands to abandon ship. The boats were soon released and lowered without any confusion, and Tom was glad to see his old friend the Chief Engineer sitting in one of the boats, along with his other engineers.

Tom's idea was to get away from the ship, as she might blow up even yet, for torpedoes were skimming about all over. The full moon was rising, throwing its milky light on to the sea. Tom went to his cabin to collect the ship's papers, but he found it in complete chaos. His desk and chairs were thrown about so that it was difficult to get in, but he found the ship's register, which he considered good enough for identity purposes; he had however to leave his gold hunter and wristwatch which he could not see about.

He made out on deck again and saw two apprentices standing at the davits of one of the boats. These two lads had only joined the ship a fortnight ago on their first voyage.

As the boat was underneath he showed them how to get down to her by sliding down the falls. They landed in the boat all right, then out popped the Senior Wireless Operator from the wireless office. He had been sending and receiving messages up till the last minute. His office was on the after end of the boat deck.

They both got down into the boat where he found that they had not put the plug in – for some reason it had been pulled off its chain and lost, so a wooden lid was hammered in which did the trick. Tom gave orders to pull clear of the ship to all boats. Then he had a good look at the old ship. The fore deck was well down in the water, but the after deck still had about ten feet of freeboard to the top deck.

After a while Tom saw the ship was not sinking much more. He knew soundings were only ten miles away, but here it was about three hundred fathoms. A corvette came up, and all the crew got aboard her, about sixty men. Tom had a word with the Captain, suggesting that his corvette might tow the ship into soundings where she could be salvaged. The Captain was keen enough, but his craft was lightly built and his mooring bollards were too small to take towing ropes. However, he said if Tom had any ideas he could have a look for himself with his Number One. Tom did so, and suggested where ropes could be made fast.

By this time the air raid was over. There had been severe casualties on both sides, and some ships had disappeared altogether. An American destroyer had appeared on the scene, and was guarding the remaining ships while survivors were being picked up out of the sea.

Tom called for some volunteers to go back to the ship with him to get two ropes out to the corvette. He got six able seamen, the Chief Officer and the Wireless Officer for signalling by lamp. They got into the boat and boarded again, and Tom slipped on the ladder over the side as it was covered with fuel oil. The sea was smooth enough, but a swell was heaving, which lifted the boat and crushed his dangling leg between the boat and the ship. It felt sore but Tom managed to get on board without further mishap. Ropes were put out, which the corvette took and made the ends fast on his ship.

Tom and his men got back into the boat again to watch proceedings, and things soon started to happen. The corvette let go the ropes and got clear. The ship's bow and stern were rising out of the sea, or up-ending, but the amidship section was sinking rapidly. The ship had broken up into three sections. On the after end was the balloon sailing high, attached to a wire fastened down to the deck. They pulled the boat well clear, and saw the ship sinking and disappearing under the sea. The balloon got as far as the sea surface when the wire must have broken, as it flew up into the air again.

Shortly after the ship had disappeared there was a heavy explosion, which set up a high swell for some time, but soon all was quiet. The US destroyer had taken the other men off the corvette and then picked up Tom and his men from the boat. Tom had great difficulty in climbing the rope net they had put over the side for them to climb up, as his leg was very painful.

The officers were taken to the officers' mess, and the ratings to the crew's mess to be cared for.

The Captain of the destroyer told Tom that he was going into Oran with the survivors. He said he had just finished a patrol duty and was returning to Oran when he saw all the firing going on, so he had come over to see what was happening.

It was early morning when they docked in Oran, and all the survivors went ashore, and lined up on the dockside. Tom had over sixty men there, and there were only two other people from other ships. A United States officer questioned Tom about the attack, the officer saying he knew nothing about this until the destroyer had arrived.

Well, Tom could not say any more, but he asked if any British officers were at this port. Oran had been taken over by the United States Forces, and no British were here, but eventually a Commander of the Royal Navy turned up. He was RNR so one of Tom's own cloth, and he happened to be liaison officer.

All of them marched off the docks to look for temporary accommodation. First they turned out the occupants of a house of ill repute to make place for the men, but eventually they found somewhere else to sleep, fortunately on a troopship homeward bound. All the officers, including the engineers and apprentices, were sent aboard the troopship and so got home early.

Tom himself was sent to the first aid station on the docks, as his crushed leg had swollen to the same thickness all the way round. He was given a note to the hospital and taken there on a very large American truck with a coloured driver.

He was landed outside the main door, and went in and sat on the settee, then promptly fell asleep. His clothes were in a terrible state. His trousers were split up to the thigh on both legs, not a brass button remained, and one of his sleeves was hanging off. To crown all he was covered in fuel oil, but he could not care less.

He was wakened by someone shouting his head off, asking why this drunk had been allowed to doss on the settee. Tom came to, and produced the note. The gentleman who was doing the shouting immediately calmed down and examined Tom, then he had all the US nurses bustling about to shift him to the best room.

The Chief Officer came up to see him, and Tom was surprised as he thought he had gone on the trooper, but he had decided that if Tom had to stay he would also remain to look after the interests of all, including the men who had been left behind. Tom thought that was very good of him, and thanked him for his thoughtfulness.

The room in which he was put to bed was also occupied by a Major-General of the United States Army, there being just the two hospital cots in this room. This gentleman made Tom feel at home at once. Tom then fell asleep and remained so for forty-eight hours. When he awoke, his leg was back to its natural dimensions, proving that sleep is a great healer.

The doctors examined him thoroughly, but reached no verdict. The British Consular Officer came to see him, but all he had to say was that he had informed Algiers, and somebody would be making arrangements for the crew. The bosun and carpenter were with the men, about twenty-five of them. The Chief Officer, Mr Minty, did not say where he was staying, but Tom suspected it would be with the men. He was a good chap and everybody liked him.

When Tom's room partner realised the state of his clothes, he immediately ordered, from the US Army Depot, a complete set of underwear and socks, and a pair of their Army boots, which were brown with very soft leather, and easy on the feet.

While in hospital Tom met men whose ships were also torpedoed in that convoy. One, an engineer who was taking passage in a Belgian ship together with some British Naval officers and service ratings who were in passage to Bombay, told him that he was the only survivor on his ship. At the time they were torpedoed all were having their evening meal in the saloon and he was nearest to the door on the deck. He immediately jumped out of the door, and on looking back he saw the roof of the saloon falling down on the occupants; it was only a momentary glimpse as he jumped over the side into the sea. The ship then blew up, and how he came out of it was a miracle. He was picked up by the destroyer that picked up the survivors of the *Indian Prince*, but he was in the sick bay, as he was smothered in fuel oil and had probably swallowed some. If anybody was lucky, he was.

Another man was an American sailor, as far as Tom could make out, but where his ship was torpedoed was a mystery to him. His whole theme was the dollars he would eventually gain when he arrived back in the United States.

A man arrived from the Merchant Navy Pool at Algiers. This pool was for holding men for supplying ships when shorthanded, and arrangements were soon made to send all of the crew to Algiers. Tom had been in the hospital about four days then, and was feeling much better, so he asked to be included with the men who were travelling to Algiers by train. When the time came to leave, Tom got ready, but could not stand long on his gammy leg. He put on his so-called uniform, much torn, and with the help of the Chief Officer got aboard the train. The PX of the US Army sent along two cases of tinned foods, which were thankfully received.

In Algiers Tom and his Chief had a room in the hotel of the Merchant Navy Pool. The men were asked if they would work on the docks for wages. They all agreed, and suitable accommodation was found for them.

Chapter 21

A T ALGIERS ALL HIS MEN, and Tom himself, were rigged out with reach-me-down suits of civvy clothes. When Tom could get about he visited one or two ships in port. He knew the Masters, as he had met them at the conferences, and they could not do enough for him, and even gave him warm underwear, as it was winter-time. In all he was treated very kindly at that port.

After about fourteen days there they were all shipped home on a trooper, carrying part of the victorious Eighth Army back to England. Another ship which had been sunk had her crew ashore, so they too were shipped. Tom shared a cabin meant for two in peace-time with seven others, but he was becoming used to roughing it by now.

It took about a fortnight from Algiers for these troopers, ex-passenger ships, to arrive home at Liverpool. They were manoeuvring all over the ocean to avoid air and submarine attack, in the charge of two cruisers.

On arriving at Liverpool the Shipping Master had to come on board to sign the men off the Agreement which had been left with them on sailing for safety. A sum of money was given to each man to see him home, and Tom received ten pounds.

He got a great welcome on arriving home, from his wife and sons. He was granted a hundred pounds from the Government to rig himself out again, and he also had to report to the Ministry of Pensions for a medical examination. He was informed after this that he had a blood clot on the injured leg, and would have to stay ashore until this cleared up, and he was awarded a pension of twenty pounds per month.

Tom had Christmas and New Year at home, and very nice, too, but after January was over he thought he had better get back to sea, so he told his Company that he was ready without consulting the Ministry.

The Company did not waste much time, as he was ordered to Liverpool to take command of the MS *Highland Prince*. Joining this ship he found her loading for Bombay, with more or less the same type of cargo as the *Indian Prince* had had. This ship was a fairly new one, having done only about six months. She was a standard ship of the Ministry of Shipping, run by Tom's company.

When leaving, the same procedure was carried out as before, attending convoy conference and proceeding to Northern Ireland with other ships to join the main convoy from the Clyde. On the way down to Gibraltar the convoy experienced very bad weather, and the *Highland Prince* rolled so much that some cased aeroplanes on deck nearly went over the side. But wires were passed around them and re-lashed.

Tom was glad to get through the Straits of Gibraltar into the Mediterranean. The weather can be very rough in this sea, but the convoy managed to reach Port Said.

From Suez they had to call into Aden for further instructions from Naval Control. Coming down the Red Sea to Aden, Tom carried on alone. At Aden he was told to go on his own to Bombay. The weather, being the north-east monsoon, was beautiful, it now being April 1944. Tom made for Bombay on the courses received from Naval Control. About ten miles east of the port, a buoy was moored. Ships had to make for that, then steer direct from the buoy to the port.

It was in the middle of the night when he should pick up the buoy, but having no light on it made that difficult. A good moon was showing when looking for this object, so Tom took a lunar sight. From this he steered direct for the buoy and, believe it or not, the first he saw of it was when it was scraping along the ship's side.

They arrived safely at Bombay, the first time he had been to the port. While discharging at this port, two officers of the Army Transport Division came aboard and made themselves known. One was a member of a shipping company closely associated with the company Tom worked for, and they often had a meal on board as their business was with shipping of Army stores, etc.

It was noticed that the next dock to the *Highland Prince* was in a shambles. There was the wreck of a ship which had caught fire with a load of ammunition aboard. She eventually exploded and all the ammunition went up with one mighty roar. It was so bad that it blew other ships in the dock up on to the dock wall. The dock gates were also severely damaged, which drained the water out of the dock to the level of the tide outside. Buildings close by were blown to nothing, and even buildings in town were severely damaged. The two gentlemen just mentioned had come down the gangway after seeing the firefighting brigade on the job with hoses playing on the fire to try to keep the ammunition cool. They were at the foot of the gangway when the explosion came, knocking them flat but doing them no harm. As they saw it, the explosion was upwards, which left a vacuum below it, and that flattened them on the ground. What a sight they must have seen when they came to. No words could describe the scene of destruction.

The *Indian Prince* was supposed to have a replacement of the cargo of that vessel, but she was sunk. Now the *Highland Prince* had the cargo. Every precaution was taken to prevent fire, but sometimes a piece of glass in the hot sun could start one. Hatches, when covered, were kept cool continuously by wetting the tarpaulins and deck with the fire hoses.

The Chief Engineer and Tom had dinner with the two officers at their hotel once or twice. It was a break from the ship, otherwise they would go to have dinner on their own at night, as it was too hot on the ship, it being the hottest time of the year between the monsoons and the ship had no awning.

When the cargo was out they went to Cochin for bunker fuel. The ship was then ordered to the Gulf of Cutch to load a full cargo of groundnuts for the United Kingdom, at some little railway head up a river, where the ship lay in the stream. An old Indian pilot took the ship up there, and a fine old chap he was. He had been captain of a sailing country craft for many years.

The time was the beginning of June, and the south-west monsoon had broken, with heavy storms and strong winds, after a very torrid day. The ship eventually got away, loaded up to the hatches, and they felt safer with such a cargo. When she came out into the open sea the wind was blowing from dead ahead, gale force, and setting up a terrific sea. She stuck her nose under some of the big ones, but Tom felt very confident with the homogeneous cargo the ship was carrying. He pushed her through it until reaching the Gulf of Aden and into fine weather again.

Aden was the next call, for Naval Control purposes and to top up the fuel oil, so that no oil would be needed in the United Kingdom. It must have been about 8 p.m. when she left for Suez, and about 2 a.m. a large 'plane flew over the ship at no height at all. The Second Officer called Tom and he came up immediately, in time to see the aircraft dive right into the sea at some distance behind the ship. After wondering what it was all about, Tom turned the ship around and made for the spot where the aircraft had disappeared.

On arriving where he judged the spot to be, he saw wreckage, so he stopped the ship and just lay there, closely scrutinising the sea around. The ship was low in the water, and if there had been anybody alive he could have easily been seen. A wireless message was sent into Aden about the affair, and after an hour or so Tom decided to go ahead with the voyage. He reported the matter again on arrival at Suez, but nobody seemed to be interested.

After passing through the Canal, the *Highland Prince* joined a convoy going through the Mediterranean as far as Gibraltar. Nothing happened on the way, but it was known that the big invasion had been successful in north-west France.

The ship was soon on her way again in another convoy to Glasgow. There was very little to remark about on that passage, but on arrival at Glasgow the Superintendent informed Tom that he was required to join a new ship at Sunderland which was just completing. After paying off the crew and balancing up his accounts he proceeded home on leave to be ready for the ship, the *Welsh Prince*.

He checked with the medical people at Newcastle about his leg injury and was delighted to be given a clean bill of health.

When he visited the ship in the shipbuilder's yard he saw about five ships which were exact models of each other. War-time standard ships, they were all motor ships, with Doxford's three-cylinder economy engine for a speed of eleven and a half knots.

The *Welsh Prince* was nearly completed, and Tom was informed that an Indian crew had been ordered, and were now flying from Calcutta. The officers were British, which included the engineers, and when the crew had all arrived the ship was ready to sail.

Chapter 22

THE INSTRUCTIONS FROM NAVAL CONTROL were to leave for Glasgow by going north around Scotland and tag on to the convoy bound that way, which Tom did. The ship had had no engine trials, the Chief Engineer being supposed to adjust the engine on the way round to Loch Ewe, where she would anchor for a day or so. Leaving Loch Ewe late at night Tom was instructed to take the passage between the Isle of Mull and the mainland, then through the Sound of Jura, and so rounding the Mull of Kintyre and the Isle of Arran into the Firth of Clyde, a most interesting passage. Tom saw numerous distilleries making the 'Waters of Bachhus', besides all the beautiful scenery of the Scottish coast which he was passing.

Coming down there, he allowed the Chief Engineer to give full speed for trial purposes unless in narrow waters. The ship arrived at Glasgow on the berth for loading more war cargo, this time for Bombay and Calcutta via Colombo and Madras.

The Indian crew were excellent seamen and Tom found them well disciplined. The Serangs in all departments were old-timers and knew their job. The butler in the catering department had served in the British Navy and seemed a very loyal individual.

The *Welsh Prince* left Glasgow loaded down, in a convoy carrying the Commodore and his staff.

The only fault of the standard ship's accommodation, including the native and European galleys, was that in black-out at night the only outlet for the foul air from sleeping men and galley smells was up the Captain's stairway, which found its way into this same gentleman's living quarters. It was a good way to dope any occupant of that room. Ports had to be closed and the outside glass was painted black. Tom could only use a small cabin, which was destined for the pilot when one was on board. This new ship however was much superior in the matter of ventilation.

As the ship sailed into warmer climates Tom and most of the crew slept on deck, which was much healthier.

The convoy stopped at Gibraltar, and made up again for further east. Passing through the Mediterranean, ships left the convoy which were bound for ports on the way, so it was a much depleted convoy which arrived at Port Said for transit through the canal.

The ship passed safely through, and from then on Tom was on his own again, and so made for Aden for bunker fuel, the ship having left the UK with the bare amount to reach that port.

Full bunkers of diesel oil were taken, and Naval Control was visited again for further instructions for the passage to Bombay. So she sailed again for that port, and the south-west monsoon was blowing full strength. This was met with after passing Guardafui lighthouse, on the extreme north-east corner of Africa, but fortunately the wind was on the quarter when making for Bombay, and in a few days she made the port, with the winds becoming lighter as she approached the Indian coast. Cargo was taken out there, but not all, as some was for Madras and Calcutta.

In his leisure time Tom liked to visit the gardens of Bombay, which were very beautifully laid out. Sitting there he often saw Indian gentlemen taking the air. He was very amused to watch them discussing some subject with great animation, until it seemed that they would eventually come to blows. Suddenly, however, the conversation would take a turn which would bring them smiling again, and they would continue their way, the very best of friends, arm in arm.

The Indians were great shopkeepers. They had all the novelties of their craftsmen in the shop windows, such as ebony elephants and ivory elephants carved out of a tusk, every animal showing the wrinkles in its hide by

SS *Welsh Prince.*

skilled marking by the carver; in fact, they were very attractive objects to decorate any mantlepiece. Precious stones, too, were in abundance. Should the shopkeeper see that you were interested in his wares he would immediately greet you as if you were Royalty, and no amount of refusal of his hospitality would put him off. His shop was there just for Sahib to indulge in looking. But should Sahib be tempted inside, he had had it, as the saying goes. Our shopkeeper always pressed a little present on to the victim, just to open business, so the Sahib would definitely lose face if he did not purchase something. Generally he came out of the shop with many things he did not know existed before he entered.

The Taj Mahal Hotel was a fine big building, and there you were provided with some of the most attractive ice-cream make-ups to cool the innards of a Sahib. Also from here one could sit at leisure and watch the passing of most attractively dressed people, especially the ladies in their native saris. Life here was far from the scenes of war.

The racecourse, too, was the scene of brilliant colours, with the ladies' dresses, both European and native, spectacular in the blazing sunshine. Race meetings were held at practically all the major cities, and the agent of the shipping company always provided three tickets for the stands, so the Chief Engineer, Chief Officer and Tom generally went there on a quiet Saturday afternoon.

The Europeans had a very select club, and made the Captain and his officers honorary members while in port. They had swimming pools, tennis and other pastimes for those who wished to indulge in strenuous exercise, and provided the men from the ships behaved themselves they were always welcome to join in the activities.

When the ship had completed discharging cargo for Bombay, she proceeded to Colombo for instructions for going on to Madras. If they knew of Japanese submarines operating, ships would go round in convoy, but generally they were on their own.

Madras was a very attractive city. There was a large staff here for Naval Control, but the ship did not stay very long before proceeding to Calcutta. Arriving at the Hooghly lightship, in the Ganges Delta, she waited for a pilot to take her up the Hooghly River.

These pilots were said to be the aristocrats of pilots. They came aboard with their own servants, including a man to take soundings with the hand lead, and they brought on board bedding and all the paraphernalia for cooking the pilot's meals.

The first of these pilots Tom met, after the ship was under way, told him that he had met him before. It turned out that they had met each other as apprentices before the first war in Mother Mary's ice-cream shop in Third Avenue, Brooklyn, USA. He was an apprentice on an

Australian-bound ship with a name like *Papitiki*. He was also in the gang who were taken to church on Sundays by Mr Billy Wood's launch, so they had quite a lot to talk about while his leadsman was singing out the depths of water.

When the ship arrived at Calcutta, the mud pilot, as he was called, supervised the tying up of the ship to buoys by hefty chains fore and aft, off Princes Wharf.

Calcutta had a lot of places of interest. Naval Control was in the old fort, which Tom understood to be called Fort William. There was the old square-bashing yard for the troops of over a hundred years ago, surrounded by offices and residences of various officers. Perhaps they were barracks in those days. Tom always liked to imagine days of long ago, if the scenery was right. Naval Control was a hive of industry, as typewriters were clattering, manipulated by very smart Wrens. Quite a few Indian girls were in their saris, topped by a Naval jacket, and very pretty they were, too.

Tom saw the officer in charge, and put his secret papers into his care. After discharging the war cargo, the ship loaded jute for Dundee, Scotland. Close by the ship was a swimming club belonging to the European population, which Tom often visited, indulging himself in the pool, with plenty of others of both sexes doing the same thing. When tired of this exercise the bar was handy for a long, cold drink.

The city was what one expected it to be after being in British hands for so long. Shops were plentiful, and the native population were hurrying here and there, very intent on getting somewhere in quick time, to judge by the way they walked. The Governor's carriage, with the Governor inside, came by once with his outriders who were very colourful Indian soldiers on splendid horses. Indeed, everything was colourful, for the Botanical Gardens had flowers of all hues and the trees had big bright red flowers.

The crew were paid off here, and another one engaged. Many familiar faces were seen when the crew mustered before sailing, and after completing loading the ship sailed for the UK.

Her voyage home was much the same as when outward bound, only in reverse. Colombo for Naval Control, Aden for bunker fuel, Suez and Port Said, through the Mediterranean to Gibraltar and convoy to the Downs off the Goodwin Sands. Here Naval Control came off to the ship and gave instructions to catch the convoy leaving the Thames for the north, to sail all the way up the east coast by a buoyed channel and when off Dundee proceed to that port direct.

The whole track up the coast was buoyed, so it was a matter of following the next ahead and keeping the buoys on the starboard hand. The dangerous part for attack was 'E' Boat alley, that area between the Haisboro Sands and The Wash. They had an attack the first time – there were all kinds of gunfire going on, but Tom did not hear of any sinkings. It was a very bad place during the early part of the war, but this was the back end of 1944. They all had to keep on the alert, and as Master, Tom could not afford to leave the bridge.

The war had considerably reduced its activity at sea, and Tom thought this was due to the considerable number of corvette escorts that had been turned out from the shipyards. They defeated the submarines, although there were still plenty about, but whether they could get back to their base was another matter. The bases on the west coast of France were of little use to the enemy's forces, as the Germans were being pushed back by the Allied armies.

Men like Captain Sloane, who had gone through the whole war in command of ships that could blow the crew sky-high if torpedoed or shelled, knew that the war was not over yet by any means, for the armies were still fighting like blazes in France, in the Balkans and just as fiercely, if not more so, in the Pacific against the Japanese 'do or die' boys.

The *Welsh Prince* made two voyages out and home and then Churchill announced the war was over in the western hemisphere. The *Welsh Prince* was still under the control and administration of the Government. She sailed out again for Calcutta, and after discharging her cargo there she was taken over for the invasion of Malaya. The deep tanks and other water tanks were cleaned out and made suitable for carrying fresh water, of which she loaded three thousand tons for emergency use in case the water in Malaya was contaminated. She then went to Madras and loaded war material in the holds, with trucks and tanks in the upper decks and on the weather deck. A contingent of the RAF Regiment boarded with officers, provision being made for them. This force was to act as policemen when landed.

A host of ships were gathering outside Madras in the Roads. A meeting was held on one of the ships of all the shipmasters, and instructions given, with ports to go to on the west coast of Malaya.

The convoy sailed, with all ships in formation. Tom's destination was Port Dickson, which is not far north of Malacca. The chart received from the conference had the beach and sea area marked off in numbered squares, and Tom's ship had to go to the particular square of the number he received.

The troop convoy had gone ahead, but Tom had not attended that conference, so he did not know much about them. Half-way to the Malay Straits, news came that Japan had capitulated. The *Welsh Prince* was ordered to Port Swettenham and given a position where to anchor. Port Swettenham was the port for Kuala Lumpur, the capital of the Straits Settlements.

A communication ship was to anchor off the south entrance, which is South Klang. About twelve ships were anchored off here. Coming through the Straits of Malaya, they saw the mine-sweepers sweeping up and cutting adrift mines which were being exploded.

The ships came to anchor off South Klang Strait, and Tom had just got himself settled in his armchair when a senior Army officer came to see him. Tom was asked if he knew the port, and he said he had been there a few times as Chief Officer and had knowledge of the Fairway Buoy and the leading marks. The officer said no pilots were here at present, and would he lead the ships in to anchor? Many Japanese ships had been sunk in the port area by British aircraft bombing, and Tom pointed out that he could not account for those. Signals were arranged for slowing down and forming two columns, and for when to let go the anchor.

The *Welsh Prince* started off first, and the other ships tailed on behind in single line, a cable apart. She rounded the Fairway Buoy which meant turning about ninety degrees, picked up the leading marks and so carried on. She had to keep close to the south coast as wrecks could be seen in the fairway. After rounding the Elbow Buoy into North Klang Strait, the signal was given to reduce speed to dead slow and form two columns, which was done by every other ship coming abreast of the one ahead, with reasonable distance between the columns.

The signal was then given to anchor, and they had arrived. The escorts had gone inside to take over and soon had the natives bringing out lighters to take the trucks ashore.

The RAF Regiment were landed and fresh water was provided to the tank landing craft and small craft of the Royal Navy. Tanks and trucks were loaded on to these craft and so found their way ashore. The *Welsh Prince* went further into the port where water and ammunition could be more easily provided.

The native Malays were very pleased to see the British. Naval Control took over, and soon three pilots arrived, and the port was made again. The Japanese soldiers behaved very well indeed, some being employed in the labouring gang.

The Chief Engineer and Tom had an opportunity to visit Kuala Lumpur one day, going up there in an old Japanese car, and the city seemed remarkably intact, shop windows being well supplied with goods for sale. Tom asked one or two shopkeepers how they managed to do this, and they explained that they had buried most of their valuables in the ground, and what was on show had just been retrieved. It looked very good after such treatment. Tom and the Chief were rather sceptical about the burying business.

The Malays and Chinese, in any case, were back in business, but for the time being they would sooner accept unopened tins of fifty cigarettes as means of exchange. Watches and all kinds of jewellery were up for sale. It could have been that they were once the property of British people who had had to depart from their homes as the Japs moved in. The innocent little natives had got in before the Japs.

It was said that tins of cigarettes brought fabulous prices, and all that could be got were sent to China. The weed must have been a luxury in those far-away places. Tom had to purchase cigarettes for the crew from the NAAFI at Madras, and in no tine they were sold out at Port Swettenham. Tom felt that there was a kind of vacuum between the change-over of authority from the Japs to the British.

The Japanese guards patrolled the Banks long after the British took over, under the orders of the British. The Japanese Army, in completely capitulating, had its problems, and it was said that some of the homes which had been evacuated in a hurry, then occupied by officers and medical men, when taken back by their owners had been found to contain complete documents of all the articles in the home at the time of occupation for whoever occupied them after the Japanese left.

In time the ship completed, and was ordered back to Madras. This time she was on her own, with no convoy. She soon arrived there, and again she was loaded with a full cargo of Army supplies: bales of uniforms, boots and utensils of all descriptions. Tom thought that India was just unloading herself of all war-time stuff on to Malaya. The ship was full down to her marks, and she sailed back to Port Swetterham again and discharged it all into warehouses. Back she went to Madras, loading this time reinforcement steel such as gratings for the runways of Singapore Airport. She had nine thousand tons of this material.

So to Singapore she went with this cargo, and was taken into Empire Dock. She managed to get in with a struggle, on account of the draft and lack of dredging during the occupation. The cargo was discharged by Japanese soldiers in charge of their own officers and several sergeants of the British Army. Those boys were certainly well disciplined, being quite meek and mild. But no doubt they had had plenty of fun before, when tormenting British prisoners.

Christmas 1945 as held in Singapore. The town was getting back to normal, or as near as possible. Army officers, bedded down in the Raffles Hotel, were still eating out of tins. Ships' agents were out again, mainly working for the Army Transport, but they were there to establish themselves for peace-time routine. Tom's company representative, Mr G. Harris, was out there, too. They knew each other well from before the war.

This gentleman had had a rough time under the Japanese. He was in Manila when the Japs took over, and spent three years in a prison camp until the United States troops released him. He was sent home via the Pacific in a shocking state of starvation, but being a youngish man in his middle thirties, a few months in the United States and England helped to restore him to somewhere near normal.

Tom had him and all his other friends down to the ship for their evening meals, otherwise they would have been on tinned foods.

The ship was ordered to Madras again, then re-directed to Calcutta. Here the *Welsh Prince* was taken off 'requisition', so she loaded a peace-time cargo for the first time in her career as a company's ship. A full cargo of manufactured cotton goods was taken, but not all at Calcutta. She had to finish off at Bombay, which meant going around nearly all of the Indian coast; then she sailed for Matadi on the Congo River, West Africa.

She had a good voyage around South Africa, and duly arrived at the mouth of the Congo. The voyage up the river to Matadi was an experience, passing through the fearsome 'Devil's Gorge'. The land seemed to be cut away to allow the river to flow through, leaving high sheer cliffs at each side, overgrown at the top by trees reaching over to meet each other from both sides, full of chattering monkeys. These overgrown trees made the gorge quite dark, while the cliff sides were constantly dripping with water, this being drainage from the land.

Eventually the ship arrived at Matadi, having been brought up the river from the sea by a pilot of Belgian nationality. A very nice little town it was too, with clean buildings, excellent roads and tidy shops. A contingent of the Belgian Army was stationed here, and a young Belgian officer and his English wife came on board to have a look around the ship, so Tom entertained them. The lady was very grateful, and wanted to talk so much about England. After being out there for quite a while, she was very homesick and was longing to see her parents.

After discharging part of the cargo, the ship left for Lagos, where she discharged the rest of the cargo. No doubt the manufactured cotton goods were very welcome as stocks must have run low owing to the war and lack of shipping calling from India.

When the ship was empty she was booked by the Elder Dempster Company to load a certain amount of cargo up one of the branches of the river Niger, which has a delta of several channels. One was the only navigable channel, and a bar had to be crossed with the draught not more than fifteen feet.

After passing over this bar the ship was met by a fleet of boats manned by natives, both women and men, declaring themselves to be pilots through this marshy delta. Tom had been warned however to take only one certain gentleman, and after many inquiries he was found to be a venerable old Negro. The coloured ladies in the boats were without a vestige of clothing, and thought nothing of jumping into the water and swimming about.

With the old gentleman to give advice, the ship proceeded on her way. There were many channels, but the old boy directed Tom through the right ones to bring him into the river. The place the ship had to go to was found, and Tom had the vessel tied up to a one-ship wharf.

The work of loading commenced immediately. It was bags of cocoa beans. Being Saturday evening when they arrived, Tom and the Chief were invited up to the agent's house to meet his wife. It was a wooden house, with tropical overgrowth around it, and there was a wooden fence to encompass the ground attached to the house. This fence was a mass of flowers, and the agent explained that the timber had taken root, and beautiful red flowers were produced.

From here they proceeded to a hall of administration, where the white man and his lady enjoyed Saturday night frolics. The resident was pointed out to Tom, his name spoken in a whisper, together with his good lady. The others, about six couples, were in business in one way or another, but all seemed to be enjoying themselves dancing to tunes issuing from an old gramophone from records which had been well used and were scratchy.

All were in their dinner suits and the ladies in their best finery. Both the resident and his lady were of an uncertain age. He had a perpetual drop on his nose, probably through catching a chill looking into his gin glass. The night was hot and clammy, but after dancing around a while a game of charades was attempted. They had simple pleasures, but they were a handful of people who kept law and order in that out-of-the-way place. They did that just by being most dignified in all their proceedings with the black man, and he in his turn respected them, probably knowing that they had no force of consequence behind them, so the white man got away with it without danger or fear. The black servants were most courteous, all in clean white uniforms trimmed with red stripes.

It was certainly a dump for the few white people who held such important positions, so they deserved their Saturday night festivity, trying to keep up their dignity and spirits with a few scratchy gramophone records, and Tom and the Chief quite enjoyed themselves in such company.

The ship sailed next morning, after picking up the cargo available. Tom intended to go full steam ahead over the bar into the open sea, which he did without mishap.

Elder Dempster had in peace-time small vessels going to such ports as the one just visited, to bring the goods to the ships at Lagos for carriage home. No doubt their captains knew these waters well.

The ship loaded up with a valuable cargo of West African produce and sailed for Manchester, England. She had a good passage home, and was painted up in her peace-time colours. After the war years of grey paint the white deck houses and superstructure looked dazzling and most unusual.

Having a good crew of Indians, the work was soon accomplished and when she arrived in Manchester all remarked on the smartness of the ship's appearance. Of course, the Chief Officer takes and deserves all the credit for the cleanliness of the ship.

She had been away for a period of thirteen months. In the meantime Tom found that he had been commended, by a certificate signed by Mr Winston Churchill, for his efforts on the *Indian Prince* when she was sunk by enemy action.

Tom's wife and youngest boy came down to the ship to greet him and all was merry and bright. Nevertheless Tom felt that he wanted to get away from ships altogether and have some rest from everyday duties, for as a ship's Captain, one is on duty all the time and is responsible for everything that happens or can happen.

Chapter 23

Tom's ship arrived at Manchester in May 1946, and he made arrangements to be relieved of his command after he had seen his Indian crew off to their home ports by a chartered flight.

The ship would now carry European crews, and the accommodation was altered to suit their requirements. Tom had to square his accounts with the owners, so when all the crew had been paid off and the balance sheets for all the money used from all the ports he had visited, including the money received by the crew when paid off, had been balanced to the last penny, he thought the time had come to lie back and look around his home life.

Another Captain took over, and Tom departed, with his wife and son, for home. There he was met by his other two sons who were making good headway in their schooling. They thought nothing of flooring the old man when describing some rugby tackle they had made in the school matches. They were fine lads and had looked after their mother well during the war. They were not of age to take any active part in the war, but the two eldest served in the Air Force Cadets in their spare time.

But all good things come to an end sometime, and Tom heard from his employers that he had been appointed to a ship, which was a captured German vessel now called the *Kent*. In the meantime would he relieve a Master on another ship so that he could have a couple of weeks' home leave?

It being mid-summer at the time and everyone making merry after the war years, Tom's second son came down to spend part of his end of term holidays with him, and he was good company. They visited all the places of interest during Tom's time-off periods, then his eldest son came for a few days, and they too had a happy time together. They had a good look over the ship Tom was to take over. She seemed all right, but the engine room startled Tom as he had never seen such a conglomeration of cylinder head valves, camshafts and what have you in any engine room.

The Chief Engineer was an old friend of Tom's, and he asked him what he thought about such an engine.

The Chief Engineer considered he could get the engine in running order when he had finished overhauling it, and the next time he saw him he was taking command of the ship.

The crew were signed on ready for sailing. Tom reported to his employers and was told he had to fly out to the United States, to Portland, Oregon on the west coast, to take command of an American-built ship, which was being handed over to the Ministry of Shipping, under the flag of Tom's company.

The Chief Engineer was to go with him on the flight; not the Chief of the *Kent* but someone else. The crew had already gone out, so Captain Tom Sloane got in touch with the Chief who was going out with him and they set off for Heathrow airport which in those days consisted of a few huts to hold the Customs and the newly-formed aircraft company.

They boarded a 'plane which was ex-RAF, fitted out for carrying passengers. The 'plane was full, carrying about fifty people, and by talking to them Tom found that they were all businessmen going after orders. The stewards were male, and one of them made himself known to Tom, as he had sailed in Tom's company and remembered seeing him.

They came down at Shannon, where they enjoyed breakfast, and the next stop was Gander, where another meal would be taken. The flight across the Atlantic was something to remember, as the 'plane was just skimming over the top of the clouds, which made them feel that they were not so far up in the air.

Coming down at Gander it was quite a sight to watch through the window as the aircraft came down through the clouds, and to see the land opening up below. New York Airfield was reached at last, and Tom and the Chief had to report at the company's office. From there they left by train for Portland, via Montreal. They were four days on that train from Montreal. They had a good bed at nights, and in the morning they had their shower and the attendant polished up their shoes. A good breakfast was served; in fact, all meals were excellent. The countryside they passed through was flat and uninteresting at first, but the little towns were intriguing. When the train was approaching the stations at the prairie towns the engine whistle would blow and if anyone wanted to get on a ball would be dropped from a mast and the train would pull up to take on passengers and mail, then carry on again. Sometimes the train would stop at some place as a regular stop, then Tom and the Chief would get out and walk up and down the platform. Once they dashed over to an ice-cream store and sampled its wares.

The observation car offered many attractions for seeing the countryside in comfort. Coming through the Rockies filled them with awe as the great mountains looked majestically down on them. The mountain tops were all covered in snow.

Some ravines they passed over were spanned by wooden bridges which formed the train into a 'U' shape, making the engine visible from the tail end. The train always travelled at slow speed over these bridges.

The men who built the railway must have been great engineers, although it was men with money to spare who were the pioneers and hired their engineers for the job. They thought big and lived big. Most of them had worked hard to gain their wealth and saw the possibility of more wealth in transporting people to the west coast in a short space of time. The covered wagon trail took months, with hardship and death staring them in the face most of the way.

Tom thought of all these things when travelling across the North American continent from east to west. Later he read books on the subject, which enlightened him on many things he saw in the United States. The freight trains which passed over these lines of railroad were the trains on which his friends the hoboes would travel in style.

They arrived in Portland at last, but there happened to be an American seamen's strike on at the time, and they would not allow the Britons on the ship until the strike was settled, so the crew were housed in some settlements which had been built for workers in the shipyards when they were building the Liberty type of ship. These workers had come from the farmlands. The housing was excellent, and kept in first-class order by the US authorities.

Tom and his officers, including the engineers, were found accommodation in local hotels. The one Tom and the Chief were in was very comfortable, more of a family place, and they were there a month before they were allowed to take over the ship, the SS *Atheson Victory*, which had been running for the Dollar Line across the Pacific. She was the latest type of standard ship the United States yards had built. The engines were turbines, and with two water tube boilers she could steam at nineteen knots, which was a tidy speed in those days.

Tom got his crew on board, and the Chief Engineer was given a day or so to get acquainted with the engines. He had a few jobs done ashore, and the boilers were cleaned. The Chief Officer had his bosun and men seeing to the lifeboats and cargo gear, so that all could be ready for commencement of loading.

Then off they went to San Francisco, to load a full cargo of canned fruit packed in cardboard cartons. The packing was something new, and to fill the ship up with such cardboard boxes was an experiment. It was certainly successful, as every carton turned out in first-class condition at London. This way of packing was much cheaper than wooden boxes, as well as being more presentable to the shopkeeper.

After bunkering at Los Angeles the ship proceeded on her way via the Panama Canal to London. They had Christmas at sea after passing through the Canal. The ship arrived in London after a fairly rough passage across the Atlantic, to the coldest winter for a long time.

The Ministry of Shipping had another food cargo, from New York this time, so she left London at the beginning of February 1947. After passing the Isle of Wight she met up with the Royal Navy, who were escorting King George VI on his South African tour. The weather was very hazy and working up to severe storms. Tom had to watch the ship as she rolled very heavily, and she had continually to be brought up to the wind and sea to avoid synchronising with the breaking of the waves. She was also pounding heavily. A thousand tons of Thames ballast was taken before the ship left London, and Tom was glad he had insisted on having this, which was taken to prevent pounding. It did to some extent, but when the really big waves came she would shoot up into the air, then come down with a wallop, shaking the whole structure. Only reducing speed avoided severe pounding.

That was a very bad passage across to New York, and very rarely could the ship go at any speed at all. Being all welded, she offered very little resistance to the sea when she was rolling, and Tom felt she was rolling a little too much for his liking.

Fast ship as she was, the passage across took fourteen days. On arriving all water ballast was pumped out, but the solid stuff had to be discharged into a barge.

The water ballast would not lessen at all from number one tank at the bottom of the ship, although water was going through the pump. It was decided to put her in dry dock, and there it was found a heavy keel plate had split with the pounding. That plate had to be taken off and a new one fitted; also it was found that she had no bilge keels. These are fin-like plates which check the ship rolling. They are fitted on the outside shell along the turn of the bilge, about eight inches to twelve inches wide, and are fitted about two-thirds the length of the ship at her broadest beam.

As such plates in this type of ship were only welded to the hull, they had snapped off during the heavy rolling. New ones were fitted to a riveted 'T' bar, which made them more secure.

The weather at New York was very bad, too, snow and ice being abundant. The cargo was loaded and off the ship went for London again, but this time the wind and sea was behind her, until she got into the English Channel approaches, then it blew hard from the east and north-east.

Tom hove the ship to, in the middle of the Channel, for two days, as he was not sure of his position, only relying on soundings. Besides, the pilots were off station at Dungeness.

When Tom thought he could sense some easing of the wind, though the seas were still heavy, he set a course for the Royal Sovereign Lightship, just on a hunch. Being night he would probably see the flashing light in time to correct his course if necessary. The rain squalls were terrific, but he made on, and, sure enough, the flashing light was picked up right ahead, so he made for Dungeness. Tom was hoping to find a little shelter somewhere if he got around the point, the wind being round to the north now. He made close in, and the pilot boat was there. The pilot boarded and asked if six others could come aboard to as far as Gravesend. No ships had been seen for four days. These pilots had been on outward bounders, and had got on to the pilot boat, but she had to ride the storm out as it was too bad to make Dover or Hastings.

They all came along, so Tom had enough pilots to man the ship. By now the weather was easing a little, and she was soon into the Thames.

Chapter 24

O<small>N DOCKING IN LONDON</small> a man from the Company came on board with an agreement ENG 19, with a request for Tom to fly out to New York immediately. And this after a lousy passage out and home. Tom wondered whether men were just pawns in a game, to be moved at will.

Apparently the crew had already gone out to the ship, the *Scottish Prince*. She was a war-built ship with a speed of eleven knots on round the world voyages, and she could be away from the UK for about two years. It was a hard decision to make. Nevertheless Tom agreed, but only if he had a week's leave first.

In due course he landed at New York and of all things he was over a week in an hotel waiting for the ship to arrive. When she did, Tom went on board and took over from the other master. The crew, who were from London, had already joined at Halifax.

She loaded her cargo for Far Eastern ports, calling at Newport News, Charleston, Panama and Los Angeles. Just as they were leaving Los Angeles Tom was on the boat deck waiting for the pilot when a crew member came to him from the engine room department. This man was a tall Tasmanian, and he told Tom that the crew demanded more wages or they would not sail in the ship. Tom told him that was beyond his power, as they had signed on at wages agreed by their union and the owners. The Tasmanian immediately ordered the crew ashore just as the pilot was boarding.

Captain Tom Sloane had his suspicions of this man, as he had been domineering the crew, promising them all kinds of things. He heard later that he was Communist-trained, put there by his party to cause discord among the crew.

The men all walked off the ship except, of course, the officers and engineers. Tom saw the agent on the quay, and was able to pass the word to him of the trouble. He immediately got on to the telephone and informed the immigration authorities, who in turn met all the crew before they got off the dock. They had come down in vans, and they gathered the crew up and took them to the immigration headquarters. The sailing was put off and the agent got in touch with the British Consul.

A cable was sent off to the owners and another came back, hoping the dispute, as they called it, would be ended amicably, or words to that effect. Armed with this, Tom, the agent and the British Consul saw the men next morning. They were brought into a hall where Tom had to do the talking. He told them the position, and hoped they would not be so daft as to listen to Big Charlie, as he was only a troublemaker and had left them all to hold the baby for him. He asked for hands to be shown by those who thought better of this action of theirs.

Up shot all their hands, and the big fellow in the middle scowled on this lack of appreciation of him. They went back to the ship in the vans, but Big Charlie told Tom, 'You have won this round, but I'll win the next.' Tom said, 'Son, you are a menace to me and to yourself and I will fire you at the first opportunity.'

Tom had a lot of trouble from that man, but he eventually had him paid off in Hong Kong and deported to Tasmania. The men had been disturbed, and could not face the two years away, for which Tom did not blame them, as they had nothing to gain by doing so.

The wireless officer was an excellent man and a great ham. He rigged the spare cabin close to Tom's room as a studio, with receiver type of gear which was all connected up to loudspeakers in every compartment in the ship. He even had a green light outside the door which indicated that the room was on the air. The officers and engineers had bought a lot of new records in New York, and Tom was approached to put in five dollars, which he did, so they had musical entertainment every evening, then quiz programmes between deck and engine, sailors against firemen, and so on until they had the lot interested. Even dummy records had been bought by sparks on which messages spoken could be posted home, which came in handy for Christmas messages. They took twenty-six days to reach Manila, and there was not a dull moment.

They arrived back in New York after a voyage of seven months and in time sailed again as before. On arriving at Shanghai it was found that the Red Army was pressing close on the city. This was when the HMS *Amethyst* escaped down the Yangtze River.

There was general scrambling to get out of the city. The *Scottish Prince* had to take two forty-five ton tugboats on deck for Hong Kong – some merchant was getting away with what he could.

It did not do much good keeping the ship there, so she left for Hong Kong. At that port Tom received orders from the home office to unload all cargo for the United States at Singapore, then proceed to New Zealand to load on charter to the New Zealand Shipping Company, for the United Kingdom.

To visit the agent's office at Shanghai was a bit adventurous, as when landed by the ferry boat at the Bund, he found the whole of the Bund area was packed tight with taxi-cabs of all descriptions, and Tom actually had to climb over the top of these to get to the office block on the other side. The city was in a panic, and people were wanting to get out in any type of craft. Junks and sampans appeared to be much in demand.

In Hong Kong the two tugboats were discharged with the ship's gear. From there an RAF launch was shipped for Singapore. This weighed only eight tons, but was about the same size as the tugboats.

The crew of the *Scottish Prince* was being depleted slowly by men being left behind in hospital. The odd man or two had to be taken on where they could be found, and the ship had to get along the best way she could.

On arriving at Singapore the ship discharged all cargo left in her and sailed for Wellington, New Zealand. Never having been there before Tom was looking forward to the trip. She proceeded to the Lesser Sunda Straits, passing on to Northern Australia, the Torres Strait, and so down through the Cook Strait to Wellington.

Tom quite liked the place. The people were very kind to his crew and he himself was treated with old-world courtesy by the agents. The ship spent three weeks there, loading bales of wool and cases of tinned meats.

Tom often took an afternoon off to take a bus ride along the waterfront and through the roads of the housing area on the hillside. He saw some very nice homes with very pretty gardens. The bus would then bring them into the centre of the business section of the city, close to the agent's office. Tom was very impressed with the way of life out there. Old buildings of the settlers could be seen, and even the house of the first Governor from England. Wellington was more British than Britain.

It was quite a change from the scramble at Shanghai and the unrest among the Chinese at Singapore, who would occasionally wage Tong wars among themselves. Although Singapore had many British troops, as a rule they never interfered. Life was much quieter in Wellington. Not so many people were dashing about here and there, although passenger ships lost a lot of their crew through desertion. What men Tom had in his crew were by now too tired to desert, however, and besides, the ship was going home.

On leaving, Tom and his crew were presented with cases of lambs' tongues as a parting gift from the Chamber of Commerce, together with a letter of thanks for the Merchant Navy's war effort. These were gratefully received, and all on board took some home, as rationing was still in force. Tom knew that his family enjoyed the delicacy of tinned lambs' tongues.

He had one week's leave after paying the crew off and settling up his accounts, after a thirteen months' voyage. The ship was discharged at London in the Royal Docks. She now had to go to New York and load there for South America, Brazil and the Argentine. A new crew was signed on, but some of the mates and engineers stayed on. Such a voyage took about six months.

Tom had only hazy memories of that voyage. He had been on that trade so often that each voyage was just a repeat of the last one, loading at New York for Rio de Janeiro, Santos and then the River Plate ports. The cargo was usually grain for home waters.

When the ship returned to Liverpool and the crew had been paid off nobody suggested that he might go home and enjoy a decent leave. Tom's whole life seemed to be centred about his ship, with his cabin for privacy. Books he had read many times over. Dickens's books particularly were the ones he could live with, and he read them again and again.

Nevertheless that was living in the past. Tom was now only a month or two short of fifty years old, and he was in no doubt that by now his family could get along nicely without him, as they so very rarely saw him. Months at sea were big bites out of a man's life.

When he did get home he was generally nervous and frightened of saying or doing something wrong, as it was not the life he was used to. His sons had taken to their studies, and he could not be part of the life of the eldest two as they were attending University. Many a time he put on his hat and coat and would sit in the park or on the sea front just to collect his thoughts. By the time he was ready to be off again he had just about made contact.

So now Captain Tom Sloane said he was going home and be damned to the consequences. He informed his owners that he wanted some leave. A new Master joined the ship just before she sailed, and off Tom went, make or break.

It was nine months after that break before he was appointed to command a vessel again, and that vessel was the *Scottish Prince* once more, after she had been away on charter to Japan and the Far East for that same length of time. Captain Tom still received his salary during that time, as he was kept on to relieve other Masters while they were in port so that they could have leave. His two boys at University had to be paid for and his youngest at a private school. Tom did not mind this, and never regretted his efforts to provide a good education for them. It might not have left much for himself and his wife, but they got by. Their life was for their sons.

He made a good home for them, so they had no inferiority complex. During this time of relieving they knew he was not too far away and looked forward to him coming home again to be in the family circle.

And so another chapter of Tom's life was written.

Chapter 25

CAPTAIN TOM SLOANE REJOINED HIS SHIP AT LIVERPOOL. Her programme now was loading cargo for Montreal and filling up with motor cars. When they had been discharged, they were to proceed to Sydney, Cape Breton Island, to load coal as part cargo for the River Plate Railways. The 'tween decks were left clear to load clean cargo for Brazil and South America. It was a very nice trade, with voyages taking about five to six months.

During the first voyage, in the middle of 1949, the intake pipe from the ship's side, for water cooling the engines, cracked and was spurting water all over the engine room. This was while crossing the Atlantic. The ship's side valve was shut down, and a heavy cement box built around the pipe. That lasted until Tom received Lloyd's certificate for this at Sydney.

They said it was all right, but he had the shore labour build a much bigger cement box, then the certificate of seaworthiness was granted.

Then on to New York. Tom now knew this city better than his own home town. To the same old pier they went, the same one Tom had first visited in his apprenticeship days.

More cars and cargo were loaded there, and so to Newport News to load tobacco leaf and cases of cigarettes. It was a nice, clean voyage to Rio, taking about eighteen days at ten knots.

Now the outlet pipe on the other side became cracked, and another cement box had to be fixed.

They never stayed long in Rio, and soon sailed for Buenos Aires, where the coal was to be discharged after calling in to Santos. One could call this a fine weather trade.

At Buenos Aires Tom would visit the owners' office every day and later drop in at some coffee shop where other captains would gather. There the usual talk was about charter parties, and what Tom did not know about such things was not worth knowing. Good friendships were made, and arrangements for a get-together for an evening meal either at the British Club or some other place of consequence. The meeting place in the mornings was at San Martin, where a hefty plate of sandwiches could be obtained.

Sometimes the charter required the ship to go up-river to Santa Fe to commence loading. This was up the Panama River, and it was here that Tom saw the Mardi Gras ceremony and was quite taken with the South American cowboys, the gauchos, leading the procession in all their glory. In the procession were carts full of young ladies, who threw coloured streamers to all the young males, who would look up into their laughing and mischievous eyes. In ordinary times these girls would be untouchable, as they promenaded strictly with their mammas.

At other times the ship would call at Rosario and load just sufficient to get over Martin Garca Bar, then finish off at Buenos Aires. The ship would then be full and well down on leaving, so that sometimes the bottom of the river could be felt as she touched, but that was of no consequence as it was very soft mud.

All the way from the River Plate to the Chops of the Channel was generally a good passage. The ship was therefore able to get a good cleaning and painting so that she looked very smart on arrival at whatever port she had to take her cargo to.

On the next voyage she loaded at Cardiff for Montreal, taking on a little general cargo and filling up with motor cars. This was November, and she sailed into very rough weather. The gales were sweeping across the Atlantic, giving the ship a shaking up.

It was on 5 November, at five in the morning, just over half-way to Cape Race, when Tom heard a terrific bang down in the engine room. The engines stopped, so Tom nipped down to see what had happened. She was a three-cylinder Doxford engine, and there was the Chief looking at a lot of broken metal in number one engine. He said the skirt had fallen off and completely broken up.

Well, that was anything but cheerful news, for the ship was rolling heavily in the trough of a very rough sea, and the latest weather report indicated a storm of Force Eleven to Twelve winds in the area soon. The Chief Engineer decided that some heavy machinery would have to be moved so that he could blank the damaged engine off.

Tom thought he had better see if he could steady the ship and take her out of the trough of the sea. Knowing about the use of trisails on a steamer, as ships had to be fitted with them in his early days, he set about rigging one.

He called his Chief Officer, bosun and carpenter, together with the sailors, and told them what to do. First they took a new tarpaulin and brought one corner to another, forming a triangle. A coil of new 2″ rope was brought up and after rolling the luff edge to stop the canvas splitting they pierced holes two feet apart, fitting beckets of the rope cut to go around the lower mast. Next they hoisted the head of the luff to a ring bolt under the cross trees, where it was well secured. The tack was drawn tight down to a ring bolt on deck. The sheet had two tackles attached, and one was made fast to the bollards to each side of the after deck. When both tackles were set up taut the ship had a trisail on the after side of the main mast, in the centre line of the deck.

A similar arrangement was set up to the foremast. This was all set by the afternoon, and the men went down into the engine room to help in disengaging parts of the machinery necessary, and securing them in case of accidents.

The trisails acted splendidly The extra resistance on the sail cloth brought the ship out of the trough of the seas, and she was quite steady. The weather was deteriorating slowly and by about 10 p.m. the wind was howling Force Ten and the sea rising accordingly. It was a black night, and the seas looked uncanny in the dark, where the white tops could be seen tumbling over in a very angry way. Just about then the Chief Engineer reported he had disconnected the damaged engine, and that he might be able to have two cylinders working. During all this they had the 'Not Under Command' two red lights hoisted.

The Chief tried the engines when he got a ring on the engine telegraph from Tom. After the Chief had found it was working (he had never done such a job before), he let her go as fast as he thought safe. She could steer now, and that was all that Captain Tom wanted while the storm was on. He kept the wind on the quarter, as that was the best way she would lie. In fact, she behaved very well like that, also the wind being on the starboard quarter was helping the ship to clear the centre of the storm, as it would be travelling fast to the north-east.

Tom was in charge of operations on the bridge, and by watching the sea closely as the wind slowly shifted, and keeping the sea at the same angle as near as possible, he found by early morning that the ship had gone round the compass one hundred and eighty degrees. At daybreak, which was fairly late in those high latitudes, the storm had cleared the ship. The sun came out, and the sea was dying down rapidly, which filled Tom's being with joy; in fact, everyone was smiling with relief.

The Chief Steward immediately had a royal breakfast laid on for all hands, as they could not have had much the day before.

The owners were informed by radio every four hours, at their request. A salvage tug was now on its way from Halifax. She had left for New-foundland and was well on her way when she was diverted to assist the *Scottish Prince* into St Johns.

The anchor cable was got ready for towing, and next night the tug's navigation lights were sighted. The Chief Officer had been giving the Wireless Officer the ship's position for the tug's guidance. All that night the tug stood by, then next morning she fired rockets carrying a small line over the ship, on which a heavier one was sent from the ship. The tug's towing wire was hauled up and attached to the anchor cable, then the cable was paid out to forty-five fathoms, and so the tow commenced, taking six days in bad weather, heavy with snow. The cable was well braced to each side of the bow with wire springs to take the weight off the windlass.

The Chief Engineer wirelessed to the owners, informing them which parts of the engine he needed to complete repairs. These were flown out to St Johns, and were there on arrival. Lloyd's surveyor was on the job, together with the Superintendent from Montreal. In one week the repair firm had the engine all fitted out again with the spare parts, and everything was in working order.

Tom remembers well leaving St Johns at full speed again, but the snow was falling fast, so he could not keep that up for long. But at least he had Lloyd's certificate of seaworthiness, giving the ship the all clear to carry on with her voyage.

She discharged all her cargo at Montreal, and was the last ship to leave before the winter freeze-up closed the port, calling at Quebec on the way down-river to load cargo. Already the navigation buoys had been lifted, and the river was freezing over. She got down to Sydney, Cape Breton, and loaded the lower holds with coal, then proceeded to New York.

On the way south, miles from anywhere, the Chief Engineer came up to Tom with the information that the white metal in the engine bearings was beginning to run out. The lub. oil pumps were not forcing sufficient lub. oil into the bearings. He wanted to go into the nearest port, but Tom decided to make for Recife, Pernambuco, on the north-east coast of Brazil.

After a few days she arrived there and the agent and shore engineers came aboard to do the repairs. After that was completed she made her way to Rio de Janeiro and then Santos.

In due course they arrived at Buenos Aires, where Lloyd's took the ship in hand again, as there was now more time to see to the engines. Defects were found in the foundations of the engine, which had to be firmly welded. The lub. oil pumping was examined, and new parts fitted, which were flown out from England. This was all done while the ship was discharging and loading, and at last she sailed for London.

A defect in the lubrication of the bearings was found after leaving the River Plate. Tom suggested to the Chief Engineer that speed be reduced to seven knots, and that was agreed upon, so she did the long journey home at that speed.

It took eighteen days to reach Las Palmas, where the *Scottish Prince* took on diesel oil for her bunkers and loaded about five hundred boxes of tomatoes on deck, before leaving to proceed on her voyage homewards.

SS *Scottish Prince*.

The weather was very good all the way, until arriving in the English Channel, where it became somewhat boisterous. She arrived in the London Docks on Good Friday, and the stevedores started right away to discharge the London cargo.

By Saturday night the discharging was completed, and she proceeded to Avonmouth to discharge the rest of the cargo, after the Chief Engineer had had the Superintendent down to see him about the troubles on the engine.

It was a very bad passage up-Channel, with westerly gales, and Tom had his work cut out to get the ship around the south-west corner of England to make for the Bristol Channel. An old and experienced Chief Engineer had been taken on for the passage, to give the ship's Chief Engineer some assistance.

The ship arrived at Avonmouth without any further mishaps, and the crew were paid off, after Tom, with the assistance of his Second Officer, had their pay sheets made out. Then accounts were balanced for Head Office, before Tom could think about relaxing. His eldest son had come round with him from London, and Tom was very pleased to have him there.

Tom had been informed that he would be leaving the *Scottish Prince* after a month's leave. Then in the middle of May he was to take passage on RMS *Queen Mary* to New York where he was to take command of the *British Prince*, a Victory type of ship, which was on the round-the-world service.

He arrived home on leave on a Friday, but on the Saturday night he was taken ill with suspected appendicitis, all the more unfortunate as Sunday was his wife's parents' Golden Wedding Day. By that evening his pains had increased so much that the doctor made arrangements for him to be hospitalised, so off to hospital he went in an ambulance. The surgeon had X-ray pictures taken, and after studying these he had Tom prepared for operation. This was carried out successfully, but later the surgeon informed him that it was the biggest appendix he had seen and was on the point of bursting. He had just arrived home after a most difficult voyage and it could have taken him any time. He would have been helpless.

Chapter 26

A FTER FOURTEEN DAYS IN HOSPITAL he was allowed out, which left him a fortnight at home to recuperate before taking passage in the *Queen Mary*. He did not feel very strong when the time came, but he said he was going, as he could not afford to lie about at home. He knew he would be away for two years, but according to Tom's way of thinking, that was his job, and he would carry it out. The doctor on the *Queen Mary* was tipped off to give Tom a look over each day.

He was glad to get rid of his appendix, as it must have been lying dormant since he was sixteen years old and had refused the operation in Brest. He had had twinges since then during the war, but doctors had said it was nothing to worry about.

He joined the *British Prince* at Baltimore, and was glad to see that the ship had a full Asiatic crew, except for the usual officers and engineers, also cadets, Malay seamen on deck and Indians down below. He had a capable Chief Officer and he himself would soon be fit after the long sea passages. The officers had only just joined the ship, and as far as he could make out they seemed new to the trade.

The usual ports were taken in for loading – New York, Newport News, Charleston, the Panama Canal, Los Angeles, and San Francisco and so on to Manila. These voyages now had scheduled sailings from all ports she would call at. Five ships were on this run, taking monthly sailings from New York.

It was a good trade, and one certainly knew what they were doing, as later on when one or two passengers were carried for the round voyage one old lady joined at New York and wanted to know from Tom if there was any doubt about the ship arriving back to Boston after a five months' voyage on the date scheduled. Tom told her the ship would certainly dock at 9 a.m. of that day, and that satisfied the old lady, as she said that was her grand-daughter's birthday and she would be there to meet the ship. Tom forgot about their little chat, but, sure enough, they docked at Boston Pier on the day stipulated, at 9 a.m. and the grand-daughter was right there on the dock to greet the old lady.

The ship was a good one, with turbine engines and water tube boilers. The accommodation was austere, certainly not fancy in any way, being a wartime standard ship built in the USA. She could do her fifteen and a half knots and a little more if necessary. When Tom joined her he saw some twisted steelwork lying on deck, and found they were the remains of the bilge keels which had been burned off. They were twisted like springs. Tom remembered he had the same trouble on the other Victory ship he had been on, so he made sure that new bilge keels were fitted, as without them she would have rolled in a flat calm, although this work was not done until the ship was dry-docked at Hong Kong. It was now in the schedule that all repairs and dry-docking would be done at that port.

In those days a great deal of the general cargo went to Manila and Japan. American capital was building up those countries again after the destruction caused by the war, it being to the benefit of the United States that these countries should be in a position to trade with them. This happened with Germany, too, for a country which is destitute and broken is no use to trade. In other words, no country can exist by living off its own fat.

The ships trading out of the United States earned US dollars for Britain. I suppose this could be called invisible exports. They spent very little in dollars while in the States, but they earned dollars in carrying goods to and from the East.

Typhoons were the worry on the Eastern trade, but the United States and Britain had weather stations at all the strategic points covering the Pacific and the islands in that ocean and anywhere else in the world where hurricanes, typhoons and winds of such description were common, so that ships had an early warning of such storms and could take such action as was necessary.

A study of the law of storms is one of the subjects for a Master's Certificate, but only experience will give the full meaning of them and their dangers. To help in the distribution of knowledge of the weather, certain ships were selected, on a voluntary basis, to send out on their wireless weather messages every six hours. For such purposes they were provided with the necessary instruments, such as a mercurial barometer, baragraph and wet and dry thermometers, as well as books, papers and forms to help the observer to give conditions and cloud formation as correctly as possible. The officer of the watch made out the message of all data required, and turned it into code form for easier transmission, codebooks being provided.

Weather log books were kept for the same purposes, which were handed in to the Coastguard offices at the first port of arrival in the United States. Any unusual phenomenon seen on the voyage also had to be entered in the log books. The US Weather Section of the Coastguards published a monthly observation book in which they mentioned items of interest in these log books, giving the name of the ship and observer, along with the position and date. When one's own observations were mentioned it gave added interest to those observing to know that they had brought up something worth mentioning.

The Far East was, of course, no strange place to Captain Tom Sloane, for he had already done many voyages around the world as a junior officer and as Master. He knew his way about as well as any other shipmaster. His voyages took him to some unlikely places, particularly around the Philippines, especially after the Second World War, when ships had to go to small places for their cargo, whereas before the war small coasting ships collected outside cargoes and brought them to Manila to be shipped on to the deep sea vessels.

It was very interesting to Tom to be navigating around the islands. There were always two or three ways to get to any particular spot, depending on whether he was navigating in daylight or night-time, as many unlighted small islands were dotted about.

In the case of loading bags of sugar, the cargo would be picked up at various ports, such as Iloilo on Panay Island, then Bacalod and small anchorages around Negros Island. At the anchorages the sugar came off to the ship in lighters. There were two other places on the east coast of Negros Island which had a 'T' wharf, where Tom had to get his ship alongside. He knew them so well that he could go to them night or day.

The sugar factories were not far away from the wharf, and a light railway ran the bagged sugar down to the ship. This was a quicker way than lightering the cargo out. Tom was always welcome at the Superintendent's house at these sugar factories. At one of these places the Super. was a Scotsman, and the other was American. These men did spells of three years before having a long leave, and were glad of some outsider such as Tom to have a chat to in the evenings. They liked to come on board and enjoy a meal, too.

The Scotsman was at Refuglo and the American at Bias. Bias was a difficult little place to get into as it was in a small bay only about half a mile each way, with one or two shoals for good measure. It was a proper mangrove swamp, and Tom had to back his ship into this place.

The sugar factories were worth seeing, as they were small towns on their own. The employees lived practically on the doorstep, with their families, and jobs were handed down from father to son – a very comfortable way of living without want. These factories demanded men of all skills from engineers to bricklayers and they were never short of skilled labour, as the skills were kept in the families.

The sugar plantations stretched for miles from the shore, and were owned by private individuals. The factories bought and processed the sugar cane, and it was quite a sight to watch this going under the huge rollers being squeezed of its juices. Nothing was wasted, as the residue of the sugar cane was used to fire the low pressure boilers, or it could be boiled and eventually become brown paper, which was shipped in rolls weighing a ton. The name 'manila' for envelopes comes from the use of this paper in making such envelopes.

The liquid from the sugar cane found its way into huge vats, which whirled the juices around inside until they thickened and crystallised as brown sugar. In another vat was a bleaching process to turn some into white sugar. That passed through various machines until it came out as the small cubes seen on the breakfast table. A certain amount of alcoholic spirit was produced in the processing. The factory had a laboratory in which fully qualified chemists were continually analysing the products and by-products of the sugar cane.

Excellent mahogany logs were shipped from the Philippines to the United States, and Tom's ship would load such cargo at a northern part of Luzon Island. The trees grew on the high mountainsides, and the loggers could be seen up there cutting down the trees. When they were trimmed they were allowed to roll down the steep incline to shore level to the saw-mills. At this port the logs were cut into planks before shipment. The one and only time Tom went there was after a typhoon had recently passed, leaving quite a nasty swell, and he had to anchor less than a mile offshore in sixty fathoms of water. He knew the weather would improve all the time, but the main problem was to pick up the cargo and get away from the area as quickly as possible.

They got their cargo and left, sailing southwards to Basilian Island, just south of Zamboanga Peninsula, another anchorage for loading mahogany logs. They were floated out to the ship, then picked up out of the water by ship's derricks and put down into the bottom of the biggest hold. They would soon dry out, being hard wood.

The town of Zamboanga, at the southernmost tip, was the Customs port for that area. Ships had to call here when loading at Basilian Island. There was an island just about a mile off the town, and the tides lashed through this channel up to six knots an hour. Tom could not rely much on the Philippine tide tables, except for the time of high and low water, and even that was dubious. He wanted to know which way the ebb and flow travelled, and the only way to find out was to go there. If the ship went through the channel at an extraordinary speed the tide was with the ship, so she had to go out to the other side and turn round to breast the tide before coming to anchor off the port to receive the Customs and have the manifests stamped and the clearance, before the cargo was loaded.

Hemp is grown on the Island of Mindanao and shipped out of a small port called Davao. These so-called ports were only where a few lighters collected. No doubt the labour for transporting and loading the bales of hemp came with the cargo from the plantations. Here again, the familiar name of manila rope comes from this hemp when it is made up as rope, as the usual shipping place was Manila.

Cebu City on Cebu Island was one of the bigger townships, but did not compare in size to Manila. One could stand on the hillside and encompass the whole of the city in one look. Tom found this to be one of the inlets for imports, which would be distributed to the southern islands by small craft.

A small island lay about one mile off Cebu City, on which was an Esso base for oils and its by-products. The ships under Tom's command often went there with cases and drums of oil from Philadelphia. The famous Spanish navigator and explorer, Magellan, was killed on this island. One of the first, if not *the* first man to circumnavigate our world, he gave his name to the Magellan Straits at the southern tip of South America. He was killed by the chief of a hostile tribe, and a monument stands on the spot where he died.

Coconut oil was shipped in large quantities from Manila, and Tom had taken many a full deep tank to Proctor & Gamble in the USA for soap-making and other by-products.

Hong Kong, on the south China coast, was a city of unlimited attractions. The ship would stay here for ten days or maybe a fortnight, which gave Tom and his officers, both deck and engine room, a good opportunity to see more of the city, and Kowloon on the mainland. The ship would either dock on the Hong Kong and Whampoa Dock or the Taikoo Dock for cleaning and painting and any repairs needed to the engines or otherwise. A complete overhaul was done here every five months.

Tom often attended the local lodge and had many friends here. On Sundays he would spend the whole day visiting them on the Kowloon side. There was a Chinese schoolmaster and his family. He had now retired, but he still lived at the school. He had been the English master. It was quite a day when Tom turned up there. A friend of both of them would drive Tom there, about one hour's ride in his car, and tea would be served by the Chinaman's daughters, of which he had three.

After tea they would visit a family, the father of which owned a good share of the taxis in Kowloon. He had a three-deck house, every floor fitted and furnished alike. His two sons were married with children, and each had a floor above him, and here the family held together. This house was specially built for them on the edge of a bluff overlooking the waters surrounding Hong Kong on one side and on the other the Canton River.

After enjoying an ice-cream here, and pleasant conversation for an hour or so, and watching the sons in the bathing pool in the grounds of the house, they would depart to see the man who kept pigeons. This man had hundreds of them, and they were kept in cages on the hillside beside a stream of running water. He employed about six men to feed and clean them. A vicious army of cats kept the place rat-free. His pigeons were much in demand by hotels and private homes as a delicacy for the table.

After this tour it was time to eat, so off they went for a Chinese meal at an hotel before Tom returned to his ship.

Ports in Java would be visited, but Batavia, now Djakarta, was the only port of any consequence. President Sukarno had many soldiers, but never paid them, so in their spare time they would come upon some defenceless European and clean him out of his cash if he had any, otherwise they beat him up just to show how they felt. The Dutch and other Europeans who were in the rubber business had their plantations confiscated and these were left to rot and overgrow. The warehouses were full of baled rubber sheet, and others held the spices of the East. The new regime did not encourage trade. Java, one of the richest islands in the Far East for producing rubber, tea, coffee, pepper, nutmeg, mace, essential oils, sugar, rattans and anything else in that line you like to mention, had dropped out of the world's trading, and this loss, of course, had pushed up production in Malaya, and also pushed up the prices of such goods in the shops at home and the USA.

On a visit to Djakarta by the *British Prince* a Dutchman piloted the ship into the harbour, with the use of a tugboat with a Dutch Master. By the time the ship left, all the Dutchmen had been fired and had to get out of the country. This left Tom in a quandary about how he was going to get his ship out, but while the authorities were considering what to do next, he got her out without any assistance. There was a sunken ship lying on its side right in the fairway, but he got by.

On the passage to Singapore Tom generally went through the Gasper Strait and then the Riouw Strait, among the islands on the Sumatra coast, then across the Singapore Strait to Singapore. It was good to be in Singapore and see the British flag flying. At least law and order was maintained.

Singapore was a great city, with plenty of life, good shops, plenty of narrow alleyways full of Indian shops, with goods on display on the pavement in front of the shops and people of all nationalities milling about on the streets and in the alleyways. Always there was somewhere close by, such as a tea house of attractive appearance, to sit in for a while under the fans hanging from the ceilings, enjoying any beverage which took one's fancy.

The cricket club was in the heart of the city, and sometimes a cricket match would be on, and time could be lazed away watching the cricketers running about in the hot sun. Lunch was always available at the club-house.

The Raffles Hotel, now coming into its own after the war years, was a good place to spend Saturday evening, sitting at the side watching the couples dancing. Tom did not dance, but he liked to watch the graceful movements of the dancers. Attached to the hotel were some very select shops, which showed goods that would not be seen in town, and they were worth looking at.

Sunday was the day to go to Johore. The Sultan of Johore had very well kept gardens which were open to the public. There was also a zoo, holding a good selection of wild animals found in Malaya.

Everybody who was anybody usually had a curry tiffin on a Sunday, so they would repair to a small hotel to partake of it. Singapore curry was quite good, made with chicken and rice.

Johore is twelve miles from Singapore on a straight road through rubber plantations and small villages. The rubber trees stand tall and straight in perfect rows. A slice out of the bark indicates that the tree is being tapped, and a receptacle under the cut catches the white milky fluid which comes from the tree. This is the sap, but also it is latex, which is processed into rubber sheets and rolled into cubes weighing about fifty pounds, this being wrapped in rush mats to make a bale for transport. A great deal of latex is carried in bulk, but it must be mixed with ammonia gas to preserve its liquid form.

Port Swettenham was the next port of call, often only for a tank of latex, then on to Penang. Tom had a friend here who was an engineer surveyor for the Government, and he often stayed the night at his home on the outskirts of the city.

One of the highlights of a stay here was a visit to the Botanical Gardens. The loading at this port was done out at anchor, then the ship would sail for Colombo or Trincomalee to complete loading.

Tom rather liked this trade, as it was most interesting navigation to the world's ports *en route*. He always found Japan worth visiting, and the ports of that country were of easy approach, with quays and warehouses well laid out. Typhoons caused much damage to the southern shores, as Japan is in the track of most of these tropical disturbances which sweep up from the Caroline Islands in the Pacific Ocean in a north-westerly direction and then turn off the Philippines or Formosa to travel with increasing speed to the north-east, crossing over Japan and disappearing over the North Pacific Ocean.

Japanese houses are flimsy affairs made of wood, and the divisions between the rooms are only beaded curtains, so that winds of up to one hundred and fifty miles an hour soon crumple them to matchwood. They are a hardy people to suffer such adversity on an average of four or five times a year, with always a loss of life both ashore and among the fishermen. The big cities of Kobe, Osaka, Nagoya, Yokohama and Tokyo are taking to building more solid structures, such as steel-framed multi-storey flats, and most of the principal buildings in the cities are now steel-framed, covered with reinforced cement. This seems to be the only type that will stand up to typhoons and earthquakes.

In Tokyo Tom saw a monument on a hill where most of the inhabitants gathered during the terrific earthquake of 1923, as the waters rose from the rivers, nearly drowning them all. Their homes had been swept away by fire and wind.

Tokyo was now a very fine city. Some say it had been built to baffle any stranger who tries to find his way around it. The motor buses were the best way to see the city, and special tours were run for this purpose with an English-speaking Japanese hostess to point out the places of interest, even to the Imperial Palace grounds, where the tourists got off the bus and were allowed to walk around and see the lay-out of the gardens. These were very beautiful, for flowers of all varieties could be seen and the streams of water had small bridges crossing them in typical Japanese style.

The main street had cumbersome buildings of banks and self-service stores on each side, as in European countries. This was Ginza Street. There were shops selling real pearls and other shops selling fine silk goods. Tom had shirts made of Japanese silk which lasted him over twenty years and were still wearable. He had his monogram worked on the sleeve.

A Japanese street which was most interesting was the Moto Mashi. A narrow street, with real old-fashioned Japanese shops on each side, built so low that the average-sized man had to bend to get through the door.

There the proprietor and his wife greeted you as if you were an honoured guest. The shop would be full of porcelain ware, ivory ornaments and Japanese pictures done on silk, which were very attractive. But the host and his wife made no mention of these worldly things. The prospective buyer was treated as if he had come to see the host and his wife personally. Tea was laid on a table, of exquisite design, and one sat down as if it were a cosy get-together of the family. Talk casually got round to the goods on sale, and then an assistant from the back room was called in, and several articles were laid on the table for inspection, as if the host showing off his treasures was a collector of such. One indeed felt very guilty if one left this man's shop without buying some article of value.

Many other shops were in the same street, with a line of goods that looked very attractive, and one would receive the same treatment from the owner at each. If a little refreshment was needed to steady the nerves small cafés were there where the gods took care of the unsuspecting stranger in search of a cool glass of beer or even a coffee. He was trundled up a winding stairway into a room where a very charming Japanese girl saw to his wants. If there was more than one of you each had a girl to attend to him. They brought your beer in a bottle and poured it into the glass, with many smiles of welcome. The glass would never stay empty while one was in their care

It was all very thrilling, but it was all part of the salesmanship which, according to Captain Tom Sloane, should be copied everywhere.

A Japanese meal was another exciting performance. It was the custom for Tom to take the Chief Engineer and Chief Officer out for dinner one evening while in port, for in Japan they had to have a meal in real Japanese style. The agent usually accompanied them, so they were well looked after.

They would go to a Japanese tea house, and before entering their shoes would have to be taken off and slippers provided for them to wear. Each took off his coat under the supervision of the hostess of the establishment, and kimonos were provided. These were put on with the help of Japanese girls, with much laughter.

Next they would be conducted to the dining-room, and one would see there a very low table with cushions on the floor for seats. In the centre of the table was a charcoal fire in a metal container with metal feet to lift it above the woodwork.

The guests would seat themselves as comfortably as possible. To a European this kind of cramped the legs, but nevertheless they squatted as best they could. While they were settling themselves the hostess was preparing the meal, which was cooked in a bowl on the table over a charcoal fire. Butter was melted in the bowl and chopped chicken, duck or meat, whichever the guests preferred, was added. Vegetables were also added for good measure. While all this was going on each guest was attended to by a young lady who took charge, so everyone had a lady to attend to their wants.

Rice wine was served in small cups or beer in glasses, and it was the duty of their attendant to see that the glass was kept full. As the party got a little more merry and self-consciousness flew out of the window, the Geisha Girls came in with their one-string fiddles. They played and sang their particular type of music, and after a few beers it sounded very good.

Then the meal was cooked and bowls filled, and each, armed with chopsticks, endeavoured to transfer the food to the mouth. After a lesson or two from their girl friend, they managed to take the edge off their appetite and called for more. The bowls were filled again and with gusto they were soon emptied, much to the merriment of the girls. When the

Geisha Girls came into the room they did so on their knees as a mark of humility to their guests. It was said that some of these girls were from good families and only served a period of time as Geisha Girls to prepare them for marriage and to earn money for their trousseau. Be that as it may they were all having a good time at the party.

Eventually no more food could be eaten or beer drunk, so after paying up, with many adieus, the guests were restored to their coats and shoes, got into a taxi which was waiting at the door, and returned to the ship, pleased to know where their bed was.

Saigon, too, was a port always called at, to load rubber, and the *British Prince* took the first latex that port ever shipped. Even in those days there was much unrest. The French were in Saigon then, and a pilot would board at Cape Saint James, at the entrance to the river, and four French soldiers, armed with machine guns, would also be aboard to fire at the Reds in the jungle if the ship was fired on.

Large stretches of the jungle were cleared away at various points up-river, where look-out stands were erected, the jungle being cleared so that any movement to the riverside could be detected. These Red infiltrators must have been perfect pests, but the jungle war had been going on for many years. Of course, the French had to leave in the end.

Bangkok was another port of call. The ship only went up the river to Bangkok once, just after a channel had been dredged through the mud banks at the entrance. The river itself had plenty of water for a large cargo ship, and was just over half a mile wide on the passage up and down, with wonderful scenery. It was really tropical jungle, with gold-topped pagodas of the Buddhist persuasion set in a cleared area, which added to the beauty of the scenery, especially when the pagoda tops caught the sun's rays. The ship did not stop there long, and soon sailed again. At other times she lay off the island of Koh Samui.

Tom had done about four round-the-world voyages, but one of the most memorable occasions of his life was when the ship was about to leave Colombo for Cochin on the Malabar coast of south-west India No mail had been received for the ship, which left everyone on board disappointed. As the ship was ready to leave, the mail arrived by air, so Tom asked the agent to rush it out by motor launch and Tom would wait for it outside the breakwater. They saw the launch coming just as they were leaving and so marked time while an apprentice waited at the foot of the gangway to receive the mail.

Tom received a letter from his wife, and an official envelope re-addressed by her. This letter was marked OHMS and was from the Lord Chamberlain. The Chief Officer was standing by him and Tom remarked that it must be about income tax. The Chief Officer indicated that he would know better when he opened the envelope, so Tom opened it and read the contents aloud. The letter asked if he would care to accept the honour of the OBE.

Immiediately the Chief Officer yelled to all and sundry, 'The Old Man has got the OBE!'

Needless to say, Tom was thrilled with this honour, but he had another six months at least to do before he would be home. He thought how his wife and sons would be thrilled too, so he accepted the honour by letter from Cochin.

He had been to Cochin many times since the war, and had made good friends with the local doctor and his wife, who was also a doctor. She was in charge of a hospital in Cochin. They must have taken a fancy to Tom as he had to visit them in the evenings while in port and have a real curry and rice meal with them in their home. They were of Indian nationality, and sometimes at these evening get-togethers all their brothers and sisters would attend, which made it a jolly occasion.

Tom was very pleased that he was accepted by them as being almost one of the family. Sometimes he would entertain them at the Malabar Hotel to a European meal, and have the Chief along with him. One evening they produced a tape recorder, which played back Tom chatting away to them all, in English, of course. When anyone makes friends out in those ports with good people, they are bound to make more by being introduced to their friends, and these friendships were to stand Tom in good stead.

He eventually completed his five voyages on this trade, and was relieved by Captain Frank Thornton, who had been one of his fellow apprentices in his early days. This captain had just completed a tour on the converted aircraft carrier which had been used as an exhibition ship touring British ports. He had been Master of her, so now he was coming back to earth by relieving Tom on the round-the-world voyages.

Tom soon arrived home by air from New York. At Newcastle-upon-Tyne his second son was there to meet him in an old Morris car of which he was very proud. He had just graduated as a dental surgeon, so he was having a holiday. It was summertime 1952, and Tom was going to have five months' leave; he had enough money to cover this without skimping. Also he was to receive his OBE in August from the Queen at Buckingham Palace, so things were beginning to look rosy for a change.

When the time came to go to the Palace Tom had a new uniform for the occasion, his wife had a new outfit, and his youngest son, who was now over six feet in height, was to accompany them. Tom would have liked them all to be there, but he had only two invitation cards. A hotel was booked and off they went to be at the Palace on 12 August.

Captain Tom and his wife and son joined the queue of Army and Navy officers and gentlemen in morning suits and top hats, which slowly moved into the Palace. Tom had stood outside the gate many times, wondering what it was like inside, and now he was to see some of its mysteries. On arriving inside, Tom's wife and son were directed to seats in the gallery of the room where the investiture was to take place, overlooking all that was to be seen.

Tom followed the others on the Honours List to a side room, and while they were standing around Tom discovered a fellow member of the Merchant Navy in uniform and found that he was a Chief Engineer from the Blue Funnel Line, on the verge of retiring. He was chatting away to him by the fireplace when someone tapped him on the shoulder, asking if he was Captain Sloane, which he confirmed. Apparently his name had been called several times and he had not heard. Instructions were given on the procedure of approaching the Queen, and Tom was leading the OBEs into the investiture room. Light music was being played by a Guards Band in the gallery.

Tom had a hook on the lapel of his coat, supplied for the occasion, and when he passed through the door an old Admiral of the Royal Navy stood as marker. He had to take so many steps from him, which would bring him abreast of the Queen, then he was to turn and take two more steps, and there he was in front of his monarch. She was very charming. She put the medal on the hook then shook hands with him, asking him one or two questions on his well-being, and then he stepped back and walked out of the opposite door. Here he was met by a gentleman who unhooked the medal, placed it in a case, and gave it to Tom, at the same time taking the hook from his coat lapel.

Tom took his seat to watch the investiture being completed. He saw his wife and son in the gallery, and gave them the high sign of recognition. They were all thrilled with the event, and after a few days in London, back home they went, but not before their young man had seen some first-class cricket at the Oval and Lord's.

Leaves are always spent trying to make up for the missing days and months, but one cannot do it. Nevertheless they enjoyed themselves. But Tom seemed to be no time at home before he was travelling west again by ship to New York to take over his old ship, the *British Prince*, as Captain Frank Thornton was not a well man. Tom's wife came over with him, and they took a holiday in Bermuda before she went back home.

So there was Tom back on the job again. However, he felt that if a man is trained to follow the sea it is no good thinking on the same lines as one engaged in some occupation ashore. The fellows ashore would no doubt envy Captain Tom his opportunities to see the world, and perhaps get away from the everyday drudgery the shore man has to undergo. Tom would have been bored stiff doing the shore man's job, no matter how exalted it was, and no doubt the man ashore would feel the same about Tom's job. But Tom could look back on his life and think of the hard knocks and experiences he had gained to make him the confident Master that he was.

Ship life is a life on its own. When men sailed in the sailing ships their joy was making use of the elements to drive their ship along, getting every inch out of her with the sails, by having them trimmed to such a nicety that no wind was wasted. It was a hard life in such circumstances. Many days and nights the Captain has remained on deck, his officers and crew too, in rounding that dangerous Cape Horn, from east to west. The men were tuned to such ordeals. When they won out, they would rightly boast about it, showing their pleasure in mastering the elements. Such feelings are still there in the present-day men of the sea.

So Captain Tom Sloane took the *British Prince* over again, for another five trading voyages around the world. His Chief Officer who had originally joined the ship with Tom was still at his old job, and was going to make another voyage with him. His domestic arrangements were such that it was to his advantage to do three years in the ship.

The Chief Engineer was still on the ship, so that two of his senior men still carrying on made Tom much happier. His Second and Third Officers were also excellent men, and so were his Engineer Officers. He noticed, on his Malay sailors' discharge papers, his own name four or five times, as he had signed the papers himself. The men were paid off and managed to re-sign again after each voyage at Singapore.

On the second tour the only difference was on the voyage back through the Suez Canal. His dentist son was doing his National Service as a dental officer in the RAF stationed at the north side of the Bitter Lake, and he managed to visit the ship each time she came through the Canal. One time he could not make it, it being the middle of the night, but as the ship passed the signal station close to the Canal, on entering the short Canal to Ismailia he was standing on the verandah of the signal station, waving, at three o'clock in the morning. Tom was able to hail him with the news that they would be in Port Said for two or three days for boiler tube repairs.

Believe it or not, that lad hitch-hiked a lift on Army trucks and met Tom when the ship tied up at Port Said, so they had two clear days together. He had arranged it with his colleague at Port Said.

When the British troops moved out of the Canal Tom's son moved over to Aden. In all he did three years' foreign service before he was discharged from active service. Of course, that gave him a taste for other countries, and now he is in Victoria, BC, Canada, with a wife and four sons, doing very well at his profession.

The British troops leaving the Canal area made it more hazardous for shipping, and the pilots warned Tom not to tie up at Port Said, on account of sabotage by Egyptian roughnecks. The ship usually tied up for fresh water, but this time Tom took her on. But somehow the fresh water was being used more than ever, so he took her into Algiers. There it was found that the ship had been losing water through leaking boiler tubes. These had to be repaired before going further, which took two to three days.

The Company's representative at Singapore was leaving the Far East. He was the man who arranged the cargoes and the ports the ship had to call at. A new man came out, and Tom's ship took him up to Singora, the southernmost port of Siam, on the border of Malaya's east coast. There he met the shippers of rubber from the Siam plantations.

None of them could speak English, except the agent, who was the local bank manager. Tom could get away with one or two words, and this, backed up with hand-waving, managed to get through to them.

At night the agent took them to a café, not very clean by home standards, but there they were, losing themselves around a huge round table, without cloths or any refinement. Presently in walked every man they had made contact with that day, along with a few Dutch planters, and they sat down to enjoy themselves. There were no alcoholic waters of any description, as they were forbidden by law.

They all got their chopsticks and bowls ready, and in came the curried chicken and rice, along with all the sauces, then a huge platter with a cooked fish which everyone attacked with their chopsticks, so that it soon disappeared to the bone. Finishing up with fruit of all descriptions, everyone was soon beaming all over their faces, then a few songs were sung, followed by everyone having to sing a tune by himself, which caused great laughter. Out came a ball of string, and they were all soon doing tricks and funny things one did with a bit of twine on one's fingers when a child. Everybody was laughing with great gusto, especially the Siamese, and Tom began to suspect they could speak English as well as he could.

Tom wanted to sail at 2 a.m. and when they came to take their leave it was close on midnight. The streets, if one could call them that, being only earth-hardened roads, were full of young men and women dancing in their special style, just gliding around to the music, with a good use of the hands, not touching each other. Such dancing always fascinated Tom, with the rhythm from pipes and drums.

Tom and his friend had to drag themselves away from the overwhelming hospitality, and they got into the launch to a great send-off by all. It was about an hour's run to the ship, and when they got on board the anchor was hove up and off they went. They sailed for Singapore, and by leaving so early they arrived there in time to clear Customs and Quarantine before dark, so the work of loading could commence right away.

Before this event, when the company's leading man was still in charge, he mentioned to Tom that one of the wealthy Chinese shippers was having a big wedding for his daughter. He and his wife were going on invitation, and Tom could come along too. It was held at a place called the 'New World', which was an amusement park, boasting a huge ballroom which had been hired for the occasion.

When they arrived there everyone was met by the bride's mother and father, who shook hands with all, Tom included. There were other Britons there too, such as dockyard people from the Singapore Harbour Board. In an offshoot space the merchant was also entertaining his labourers and their wives. The couple had already been married, and this was the reception. Each party was at its own table enjoying bottles of famous brands and food served in abundance, using chopsticks.

Then came the toasts. First the bridegroom went round all the tables, glasses would be filled, and one had to watch the waiters as they would fill one's glass with the pure stuff. 'Yam Sing' was the call, as the young man and his attendants came to the table, and anything in one's glass had to go down at one gulp. Next the bride came round with her maids of honour, and the Yam Sing, 'bottoms up' in other words.

Then the party was over and the bride and groom were bidding everyone goodbye, receiving all the good wishes from the guests. Tom enjoyed himself, but felt glad that such affairs did not happen every day.

In due course he did his five voyages, taking about twenty-five months, then he took his leave again.

Chapter 27

A FAVOURITE TRACK FOR TYPHOONS, which are similar to the hurricanes of the West Indies, would originate down by the Island of Yap in the Solomon Islands in the Pacific Ocean, proceeding slowly towards the Island of Guam in the Marianas Islands, increasing in intensity and speed along the track towards the northern part of the Philippines – the Island of Luzon. They may then curve towards Japan or move over the inland waters south of Luzon, and these typhoons developed at least five or six times per month.

On one voyage on the *British Prince*, during Tom's second tour, they had just passed the northernmost island of the Marianas bound for Manila from San Francisco when one of these tropical storms was reported by Guam on the weather warning. Tom was making for the San Bernardino Straits on the eastern side of the Philippines south of Luzon, which is about three days run at 15 knots. This disturbance was on a track which would strike the area they were making for at a speed of 12 knots WNW. The force of wind was given as 150 miles per hour near the centre, something no ship could stand up to. Tom was in a quandary whether to carry on or go around the north of the island of Luzon. He was a day ahead of the typhoon if it maintained the speed of forward motion going via the San Bernardino Straits. If it did cross south of him by going north of Luzon Tom would still be in a fix as it would be impossible for the ship to make Manila for another week, so the ship was kept going on the south-easterly course. The United States weather predictions for typhoons were very good as they sent out aircraft to keep a check on the centre of the storm, which they did with all such cases, and kept shipping well informed.

As the ship was approaching so was the storm, but fortunately, they made it a day before the typhoon struck the area, their ship being safely tied up in Manila. If the storm came over Manila would be in a bad spot again. It did pass over the inland waters and lay some distance west of Manila Bay, having slowed down in turning to the north, then to a more easterly track. Much damage was done to the islands in its passage, and many fishermen were drowned. The rain at Manila was terrific, and the atmosphere was dense with spray and mist, being in close proximity to the storm. Being alongside the quay was something with all moorings out, and water rising under the influence of the typhoon, but that was better than being knocked about by tremendous waves in the storm. After three days the disturbance moved away to the north, for Japan. If Tom had taken the northern route he would have had to spend many days extra at sea before making Manila. Much fuel oil would have been used to avoid contact with such a storm.

After his second tour on this service, Tom came home for leave. A happy time was had at home with his wife and three sons. It was a warm and sunny summer in 1955, and he thought it was all well worth his going to sea and earning a little extra money on longer voyages to have such grand reunions.

After two months at home Tom had the offer of a fairly new ship built at Vickers Naval yard on the Tyne about two years previously, the motor ship *Cingalese Prince*, joining at New York on the same trade as the *British Prince* around the world. He accepted this berth and went out by air from Prestwick, Scotland. Tom's wife and sons came up to Newcastle by car to see him off in the train, their youngest son driving.

When Tom had been in Singapore on his last tour he had made arrangements to purchase a car for his next leave, although he had no licence. All his sons could drive and had passed their tests. One had an old Singer model, the next one had a motor bike and the youngest had a 1936 Morris. His wife had mentioned in one of her letters that she hoped Tom would buy a decent car for the family, so he went to a Ford agent in Singapore and started paying so much each voyage until he covered the price of a new car, without tax. The last time he was there he collected all the papers for a car to be picked up in London.

This gave him an untaxed car for six months. It would have to go out to Singapore after that, and he would probably get nearly full price for it. He would only add the tax to buy a new car at home. It worked all right, and Tom had a car of his own. Between times, when he was on leave, he passed his test, and when he was away at sea his boys used the car.

His leave with a car was something indeed. They enjoyed the countryside and all were happy. Great days those, when fellow motorists were most polite and lorry drivers were the most helpful people in the world.

But this leave did not last long, and in two months he was flying out to join the *Cingalese Prince*. This was one of the newer ships, built in 1948. She was a motor ship, which did not appeal much to Tom, as he had had a lot of trouble with motor ships, but taking it all in all, one ship was as good as another to him.

They sailed to the usual ports around the coast of the United States and out East. The difference with this ship was that she carried twelve passengers on the round voyage. The passengers were American and generally over sixty Tom enjoyed their company and made good friends with several of them.

They did three voyages around the world, about fifteen months away from home, when one of the other ships on the trade which had been home for engine overhaul, came out and took our next sailing. The ship *Cingalese Prince* was left without a sailing from New York, but a charter was fixed to load a full cargo of sugar from Cuba to the Continent. Before leaving New York another charter was fixed from New York to Cuba, general cargo and American cars. They carried this charter to Havana on the north of the island. After discharge they proceeded to another port on the south coast — Conception — to load sugar.

The time was near to Christmas 1956 and the ship was down to sail on 28 December. It was Christmas night, and Tom was still listening to his radio, to the programmes from the United States. *Holy Night* had a fair monopoly of the music on the radio, together with a new song, something like *What Will Be, Will Be*. He had just switched the radio off and was preparing for bed, when a knock came at his door. Tom went to see who was there, and found a local policeman with a telegram. He read: 'Come home immediately. Jim happened a fatal accident,' signed Robert, his eldest son; Jim was Tom's youngest boy. A note also with the policeman was from the telegraph office, to the effect that Tom would have priority if he wished to send any message; he had only to go to the telegraph office. A taxi had been sent down for him.

Tom was dazed, but slipped on his clothes and took advantage of this fine offer. To the telegraph office he went and sent a message home, giving some idea when he would be home and his condolences to his wife and Robert. His second son was in Victoria, Canada, and had been there only two or three months. Tom found out that all that had been done for him was through the kindness and generosity of the telegraph operator.

He walked the decks all night, waiting for daylight so that he could get in touch with his agent at the port, and the day being Christmas was going to make things somewhat difficult. Anyhow, Tom got through to him on the telephone and arranged to meet him at 8.00 a.m., then informed the chief officer that if he could get away the Chief Officer was to take over command of the vessel and come ashore with Tom to the agent and have his name put on the register at the British Consulate.

A telegram had been sent to the owners in which Tom asked for permission to leave and giving the reason. As the ship was not leaving for four days they had time to send another Master out. Tom considered that he had been a good servant to them, so they could help him out. If the ship had left on her normal voyage she would have been in the middle of the Pacific Ocean and Tom could not have done much about the matter.

When Tom saw the agent he had a flight arranged to New York, where he could at least contact somebody, and he could leave immediately. He spent an hour or so instructing the Chief Officer on the track he had chosen to clear the islands and cross the Atlantic to Antwerp; he was also to see the British Consul on the Monday. Accounts and all ship's papers were handed to the Chief Officer. Tom left in the afternoon and was glad to get moving. Next morning he was in New York, 26 December, and arrangements for a flight to London that night were made. Everybody was very helpful – a cable came in from London on the Telex, in which Tom was given full permission to proceed on his journey.

Tom was back in his own home on the evening of the 27th. It was a terrible home-coming. His second boy was on his way from Canada. The funeral was on the Saturday, and there was a big vacuum in the family circle.

The ship duly arrived at Antwerp and after the cargo was out would go back to New York. The company suggested that Tom's wife might make the voyage with him from New York, so she went out by air to join him when he arrived back in the United States. His old Chief Officer came back with the ship, too, and the Chief Engineer had his wife out as well, so they all looked forward to the voyage. At Los Angeles Tom's second son came down from Victoria, British Columbia, to see them. He was in a good practice at Victoria, as mentioned earlier, after three years as an RAF dental officer.

They had a good crowd of passengers that voyage, so the wives had a wonderful time, his wife doing shore excursions with them when Tom could not get away. This was the first time he had been accompanied by his wife, and he could hardly believe she was there with him.

She accompanied him back to New York, and then to Los Angeles again, where their son met them and took her back to his place, to attend his wedding to a girl from home. In all she was away from England for seven months.

Tom made another voyage and so completed his tour on this trade again, arriving back home in November 1957.

It was March 1958 when he had a telephone call from the Head Office. The Chief Superintendent requested him to have a look over the company's new ore carrier, which was discharging ore in the river Tyne. He went as directed, and found that the Captain was an old friend of his.

They were delighted to see each other again, and Tom was shown all round the ore carrier. She was certainly well equipped, and had extraordinarily good accommodation for all the crew, with single cabins for each man on board. The men had a large mess room with its own pantry where food could be kept hot, and a recreation room for entertainment.

The new MacGregor steel hatches were fitted, and she had everything to make a ship comfortable. No worries about the stowage of cargo as in his last ship, with ever so many different commodities which could not be stowed together. This ship had only one class of cargo – iron ore – and it was poured in down a chute.

When Tom arrived back home he was filled with envy for his old friend who had such a comfortable ship. But he wondered why he had been sent down to look at her. Fully expecting that he would be going back on the Eastern run again, he got on the telephone to Head Office and thanked them for inviting him to see the ship, and told them how eager everyone was to show him around. The Super. asked if he liked the ship, and Tom replied that he wouldn't mind such a ship himself. The Super. then said, 'Well, you've got one,' and told Tom he was to join the next new ore carrier at Glasgow where the final touches were being carried out to her fitting-out.

Tom was delighted, and couldn't wait to tell his wife. In a few days' time he was sent up to Glasgow to take over the ship when she was ready. The time came for her trials, which she took in the Firth of Clyde. The Managing Director of the Prince Line was there, together with directors of the shipbuilding company.

As all this business was in the hands of the shipbuilders, he had to wait until the directors decided to take the ship. She was at anchor off Gourock when Captain Tom hauled the shipyard flag down and hoisted his company's flag. Mutual congratulations were made all round, the shipyard people left and the Shipping Master from the Board of Trade offices boarded with the crew for sailing. The ship's Register was brought up from London by one of the staff and handed over to Tom, who signed it in front of the Customs Officer and Shipping Master.

Tom was now Master of this fine new ship, and as soon as the crew had signed the agreement he went on the bridge, rang standby on the engines, hoisted up the anchor and so put the engines ahead and she sailed out of the Clyde for Warbana, Newfoundland. The ship was well ballasted for such a voyage, carrying about eight thousand tons of water ballast. This water could be pumped out in four hours, ready for loading.

She carried fifteen thousand tons of iron ore, and her navigating bridge, engines, and all accommodation were at the after end of the ship. She had all the latest navigation equipment; in fact, she was the last word. Her name was *Edenmore*.

The weather was very rough going across, and the seas were breaking right over her. The other ship, too, was making across at the same time for the same place, and on arrival at the port Tom found the sister ship there and they were able to exchange greetings. They went under the tip

SS *Edenmore.*

first and loaded up in seven hours, and the *Edenmore* followed to load her first cargo of fifteen thousand tons of iron ore for Glasgow, taking the same time as her sister ship, who had been loading for Cardiff and had already departed.

The voyage back to Glasgow was like a pleasure cruise, as the sea was as smooth as a park lake. When she arrived back in Glasgow under the iron ore cranes she was thoroughly examined by the superintendents and the shipyard people for defects. Little was found to be wrong in her, and soon she was discharged and sailed for Seven Islands in the St Lawrence River. After another rough passage they duly arrived at their destination. Tom did not see any pilot around so pushed into the port. Inside, a tug took them in hand by tying up alongside and putting a pilot on board. Now they were in the tug's hands, and they pushed the ship alongside; only one rope was put out each end. All the steel hatches were open and two big chutes were lowered down over the hatches and started shooting iron ore into the holds. The tug just moved the ship along the berth as the hatches were completed.

Two big blackboards were placed at each end of the ship on the quay, where the draft was marked as the ship went down in the water, so that from the bridge the draft could be seen at any time to check loading. Before loading commenced the chief officer had given all particulars about the amount of cargo the ship would lift, and the draft to finish on. When finished, the steel covers over the hatches were soon drawn and secured, the ropes having been stowed already. Papers were received, and they were now all ready to go. The tug just eased the ship off the wharf and placed her head for the passage out of the harbour, and so they left on their voyage, to Cardiff this time.

They had a beautiful passage home, the sea as smooth as glass, and made Cardiff as the sister ship was coming out. After docking – not under the crane grabs as a ship was already there – Tom was surprised to find his wife had come down from Newcastle. Luckily they had a full day in port. Tom was really pleased that she had made that long train journey to come and see him; anyhow, it was a change for her.

Fortunately, the iron ore berth was occupied, so they had the night and all next day together, but then off Tom went to Seven Islands again.

The turn-round was as before, with no time wasted, and in a few hours the ship was loaded and on her way out of the port, with fifteen thousand tons of iron ore. They were low in the water, and the sea went over her from one side and overboard on the other. There was a tunnel under the deck, by which the men could go forward without having to go on deck, also the steel hatches could be examined for any leakage.

Tom and his men thought nothing of the heavy seas washing over the ship, as there was nothing to damage. She was now bound for Cardiff again. Half-way across, Tom received a wireless message from the owners, saying he had to leave this ship on arrival at Cardiff and take over command of the *Javanese Prince* at New York, as the Master there was ill.

Captain Tom did not fancy the change-over, as shipboard life was entirely different on the home trading ship, with not so much ceremony. And now, they said his passage was booked on the *Queen Mary*, so there he was going. He sent his gear from Cardiff to Southampton, and went home for a few days. He took passage on the *Queen Mary*, and on the crossing he was often invited to the Staff Captain's cabin and so met the Captain himself and the officers. He had a table to himself in the dining-room.

Soon they arrived in New York, and Tom joined the *Javanese Prince* and took over command. The previous Captain was ready to go home, and Tom understood that he had developed sugar diabetes.

Once again he was on the round the world trade, visiting ports in Japan, China, the Philippines, Saigon, Bangkok and Singora, Singapore and other ports up the coast, Ceylon and the Malabar Coast and Cochin.

On the third voyage round Tom heard in Hong Kong that the ship was coming off the Far East trade when she arrived at New York. On the Sunday he was having the day off with his Chinese friend, visiting other old friends, and when he went to the hotel in the evening for chow, he found all the friends he had visited assembled at the hotel. They were giving

Author boarding SS *Javanese Prince II* at Halifax, Nova Scotia.

Tom a dinner, knowing he would not come back that way again. He found the Chief Officer and Chief Engineer there too. It was a real Chinese meal, and speeches were made, with everybody saying nice things to Tom. He

Author with a great friend of the same name. Halifax, Nova Scotia,
SS *Javanese Prince II* 1959.

replied in the appropriate manner, and after saying goodbye to them all, Tom and his Chiefs departed to the ship with mixed feelings.

When the cargo was out at New York the ship took a charter to load hogsheads of tobacco leaf from Newport News, Virginia, for Avonmouth and Liverpool. While she was discharging at Liverpool, a dockers' strike occurred, which delayed the ship, so losing another charter for a similar cargo. Tom went home on leave, thinking that was the end of the Far East trade for him.

This was October 1959. At the end of November he received a telephone call from the Chief Marine Superintendent, asking him if he would fly out to Colombo to take over the *Eastern Prince*, whose Master had been left in hospital at Singapore, the Chief Officer being in temporary command.

Tom took the plane on 5 December 1959, arriving in Colombo the next day, and so joined the ship. This was the last ship to go on the Far East trade.

The Chief Officer was a very fine officer and gentleman. He had the previous Captain's accounts all up to date and posted them off himself, so Tom had only to worry about his own accounts. There were the usual twelve passengers on board, all good people – retired folks.

As the ship would be going to England the Asiatic crew was asked to carry on, and they would be flown back to their homes from there, but nobody seemed to know what they were going to do, as no new crew had been ordered. Cochin being the next port, Tom just let the matter drop until they got there. The crew knew there would be no reliefs, but some wag had been egging them on to demand their release.

Arriving at Cochin, the trouble started when all the Goanese stewards and Indian engine room staff staged a sit-down strike and demanded to leave. The Malays were all right, as they had an understanding when they paid off and re-signed at Singapore. The twelve passengers were put ashore into the Malabar Hotel as the cooks and stewards were on strike. The Shipping Master at the port was consulted and he tried to persuade them to carry on, as it would take some time for new men to come from Calcutta and Bombay, but they were having none of that.

Tom was seeing his friends, the doctor and his wife, and casually told them of the difficulty of obtaining new men. He felt that surely there must be suitable men at this port instead of having to go so far afield for them, and the very next day a man came on board looking for a job. He had a proper seaman's book, so was asked if there were any more of his kind, and he said there were. Now the job was to get a butler, as the head man of the catering department was called, and also a certified ship's cook. The doctor got in touch with the manager of the Malabar Hotel and others; soon he had both ratings, also a serang for the engine-room. These men would find a crew between them, and soon they had all that was necessary, ready to sign on the ship.

All looked rosy now, but, believe it or not, the old crew would not leave the ship and be paid off, so with the help of their old friend the Shipping Master, who had spoken to the men who were still refusing to work and refusing to allow the new crew to board, they went to the police, much against the grain. The police, however, could not do anything until they had orders from the head of the State, so Tom had to go and see him to gain permission to use the police to remove the old crew. He took the agent along with him, and had to drive many miles outside the town to his residence, where they found him, like any ordinary man, entertaining his children.

After all had been talked over, and Tom had satisfied him that the men had not been ill-treated, and that all had been done to satisfy them, he gave the order to Tom to have the police remove them. This was done, and the old crew were soon removed by the police.

Chapter 28

THE NEW CREW WERE SOON ON BOARD and took over the catering and stewards' department, as well as the engine-room.

Although some of the men had not been to sea before they shaped up very well. The Captain's steward was one of those who had not been to sea, but Tom was highly satisfied with his work and his cleanliness.

The ship was now fully manned, the passengers came back on board and she was made ready for sailing. She had been delayed for two days, but in that time more good-paying cargo had kept coming alongside and being loaded The *Eastern Prince* was well down to her marks; in fact, it was a good thing she was leaving, as she would have been below her marks before long, it being very hard to turn good cargo away when it was offered. However, the weather across the Arabian Sea would be favourable, as the good monsoon from the north-east was blowing.

She sailed just before Christmas, that day being spent in the Red Sea, and arrived safely in New York after visiting Halifax, Nova Scotia, and Boston, USA, and that was the end of the Far East trade for that ship.

After the cargo was discharged she was chartered to load newsprint from St John's, New Brunswick. She arrived there at the beginning of February 1960 and loaded a full cargo of heavy rolls of paper for Manchester. In due course she reached that port to deliver her cargo, and all the Indian and Malay crew were sent to their home ports, by chartered aircraft.

Captain Tom Sloane now had some leave to work off, but he was given the choice of staying in the ship or taking over another which had been chartered by Shaw Savill for a period of ten years.

The *Mystic* was only one year old, and was on the New Zealand and Australia trade from home ports. Captain Frank Thornton had been in conmmand of her, but had to leave owing to ill health. Tom gladly accepted the offer, as he was well into his sixty-first year and had never been to Australia, and only once to New Zealand. So it would be something new to him, and he was most anxious to see those countries before he retired, especially as he would be trading from London and Liverpool. Conditions for leave and shipboard life had changed considerably since Captain Tom first went to sea. Now regular leave was looked forward to on arrival in a home port. A relieving Master and officers took over while the voyage men had that leave, and their duties often took the ship all round the coast before the regular men were called back to take the ship on her next voyage. Captain Tom Sloane was having his first taste of this while on the *Mystic*.

She was a grand ship, her accommodation for the crew being arranged similarly to the ore carrier *Edenmore*. After two months' leave he joined the *Mystic* at London, and Tom liked everything about her.

Her first voyage was down through the Panama Canal, then across the Pacific Ocean to Auckland, New Zealand. In this country they were more British than in the UK. The weather was wonderful, and the shore staff very nice people to deal with. The main street of Auckland ran right down to the docks; Queens Street, as it was called, had a very handsome Post Office building and the shops lining each side of the street were well worth looking at. Numerous coffee houses were tucked away between such shops, where one could relax and drink the beverage in pleasant surroundings.

Halfway up, on the left-hand side, was the University, with extensive grounds which Tom was told belonged to the local Authority. They were laid out for the citizens to relax in, with nice flower beds and even a flowered clock, a copy of the one in Edinburgh, Scotland. There were plenty of seats on which to sit and admire the surroundings, generally placed under trees for shade from the hot sun in that sub-tropical climate. In the course of time he found he had friends from home living in one of

The command, navigation and administration department of the ship.

the suburbs of the city, and it became quite a treat to go and see them while in port.

There were many excellent schools on the outskirts of the city, where Tom often watched the schoolboys playing rugby under the watchful eyes of an instructor. It was the national game, so the boys played with great keenness. No wonder the All-Blacks are the best players in the world.

Tom made up his mind to find out all about this lovely country, so he visited a bookshop at the upper end of Queens Street, where there were books galore, all new, in a very well set out shop. Any subject one liked was there. So Tom bought a book by a Mr Reed on New Zealand, not forgetting Captain Cook's voyages and the wars with the Maoris when the emigrants were looking for land on which to settle.

The company to which Tom's ship was chartered, Shaw Savill, started in business by shipping emigrants from England to New Zealand in sailing ships; indeed, the history of this company is the history of the settlement of New Zealand before the country became a Colony of the Crown.

Private companies who had purchased huge tracts of land from the natives at prices which dazzled these simple folk, wanted the land populated by British people. Their agents in the British Isles went looking for such people and generally found them on the farms where the ordinary working man was fed up with his lot at home. They invented the slogan 'eight hours' work, eight hours' play, eight hours' sleep' to attract them and help them to make up their minds.

Sailing ships were chartered to take them out, and after suffering the hardships of a voyage around Cape Horn, or running the forties down in the horse latitudes among icefields and such-like hazards, they were ready for anything on arriving in the land of milk and honey.

But the Maoris objected to such an influx of white people, and soon they had a war on their hands. The British Army from Australia had to come over and help out until the Chiefs of the Maori people agreed to the Great White Queen taking them under her protection. It is said that the Maoris were perfect gentlemen when attacking stockades containing the British people, and the story goes that when they ran out of food or ammunition they provided them with more so that they could keep on fighting. Great events certainly happened during the nineteenth century.

Auckland is a beautiful city, with its racecourse, green belt, University, beautiful homes and countless gardens, well laid out shops and now a superb airport. Its docks were clean, with deep water right up to them. But this was only one port. Tom had others to visit.

Wellington, at the southern side of the North Island on Cook Strait, was once the capital of the island. Its Government buildings, all built of wood, set out in well laid out grounds, including the residence of the first

Governor, were still standing. This residence was now a museum, which anybody could visit. Wellington is often known as 'Windy Wellington', owing to the high land surrounding the bay, which encourages down-draughts of air of no mean force.

Passing down to South Island the ship came to a little town with a few wooden jetties for ships to tie to. This was Lyttleton, which lies in a bay on the north side of Banks Peninsula, named after Banks, the botanist who accompanied Captain Cook. Littleton is the sheltered port for Christchurch, and it was here that the emigrants of English origin landed from the sailing ships. They had to climb a high hill, and the path they used is still there and is called the Pilgrims' Walk. At the top is a statue of a woman emigrant looking over the great stretch of green plains on the other side of this hill, or mountain, as they choose to call it.

These are the Canterbury Plains, and now these plains were the grazing grounds of thousands of sheep, and what sheep they were, for this is where the Canterbury lamb came from, together with the large amount of wool that was shipped all over the world.

Christchurch was a city worth seeing, with its magnificent cathedral in the centre, and the beautiful river Avon flowing right through the city, with lovely beds of flowers surrounded by well kept lawns. Ducks and their chicks swam about with no one to molest them. God knows if such a stream could be maintained in an English town with the same results.

On one side of this stream was the edge of the green belt, where one could stroll for miles in the shade of trees. Here and there one came across a building where a cup of tea could be obtained, and refreshing fruit drinks. The picnickers had everything, and no litter was seen anywhere. Birds gave their calls, and ducks preened themselves alongside small streams. What a place for the wanderer!

The homes were bungalow type, all with magnificent flowered gardens, many of these gardens running right down to the River Avon in the residential area.

Tom found that folks had no need to climb over the mountains to reach the Canterbury Plains or the city of Christchurch, as the mountain was tunnelled through to provide a railway. While Tom was there it was only a railway tunnel, but now he believes there is a road tunnel too.

Further south was Dunedin, of pure Scottish flavour, as here was where the Scottish emigrants landed. The passage up to this city was by a natural channel, passing Port Chambers on the right-hand side near the sea entrance. A pilot took the ship up this channel, and many small islands were passed close to. The surrounding scenery was quite picturesque.

In the centre of this city stood a magnificent church, around which the city was built, more or less on the same style as Christchurch. The tall

A painting of *Edenmore* by Bruce Clark.

steeple of the church in Dunedin, seen reaching for the sky in the city centre, no doubt symbolised the spiritual lives of the inhabitants.

As much as cranks in our country disdain the church, Tom had brought home to him more than once that the church is the backbone of our civilisation. It is also the roots of our law and order, not man-made bills passing through Parliament.

The ship would call at the Bluff, right on the southern tip of South Island. There they had only two wharfs for ships, but Tom believes that now there are modern warehouses and docks. The Bluff had not much to offer in itself, except some pleasant walks round about. It had one main street, one-sided, as it faced the wharfs. Many nice bungalow homes were situated about the area, with cultivated gardens. It was the port for Invercargill which was quite a large town. It boasted an excellent golf course, another sport which the New Zealanders excelled in, as they started playing in their childhood.

From here the ship might go to New Plymouth, which is to the south-west of the North Island in Taranaki County another lovely small city, with Mt Egmont standing up in a sharp peak, like an inverted cone. Here a man could have his bungalow, a car and a motor boat. The ship lay close to the beach, and on a Sunday the cars came down, towing splendid motor cruisers, which were run into the water and soon everyone was cruising at speed all over the place.

There are many other places of interest, and Tom visited them in the course of his duty. Nelson was not a very large town, but he never saw so happy and hospitable a set of people in all his life.

After her outward cargo was out the ship would load wool at most of the ports mentioned, together with canned meats and fruits. The Shaw Savill Company was a household word with the New Zealanders, coupled with the New Zealand Shipping Company. These companies must have been the means of populating the country, and feeding and clothing the people. In the early days it was a long journey from the British Isles, travelling on a sailing ship.

An old custom of these ships, going back to the emigrant days, was that a doctor was always allowed a free passage if he gave his services to the emigrants, and many a doctor of medicine has landed with his fellow emigrants and has become the protector, counsellor and organiser of those poor people. Without him they would have died in this new country.

One voyage the ship loaded in London for Apia in Samoa, and from there she went to Suva in Fiji. This was a very beautiful town. The islands were very attractive, and Tom saw a few of the native villages, with their mud huts with cone-shaped roofs, made of the long grass which grows out there. He came across a small museum, and in there saw relics of HMS *Bounty*, including an anchor and burned timbers, which had been dredged up where the ship was set on fire and sunk at Pitcairn Island.

Also on view were long-handled forks for eating human flesh, which the cannibals used after their wars. To Tom it appeared that the island was under New Zealand protection.

On the same island was a small town, Viti Levu. To get there meant some miles inside the coral reefs. The ship only anchored off the town and left the following day for Auckland, New Zealand. This was a perfect trade to be on. It beat everything Captain Tom had seen before.

For New Zealand the ship loaded at London, but at Liverpool for Australia. Tom was exactly three years on the *Mystic* and each voyage was five months from leaving the UK to arriving back there. The ship did three voyages to New Zealand and three voyages to Australia, with full cargoes out and home.

To Australia the re-opened Suez Canal was used, arriving at Fremantle, the port for Perth, a very fine city with magnificent tall business houses and wide streets, and here and there arcades where cosy little shops carried on business. They had stretches of green belt called the King's Gardens, and from here, as it was some height above the city, the river from Perth opened out to quite a large lake where folks could sail their boats, water ski and do all that can be done on a placid wide inland lake, without fear. These people out there had the life and the means to enjoy themselves.

Their homes had beautiful gardens with large lawns on which water was sprayed all the time to keep the grass green. The bowling greens took Tom's fancy. The clubhouse attached to a bowling green was a place for social gatherings. In fact, it was a must to be a member of such a club or other sporting clubs if one wanted to join in the social life of the town, and the same applied to most towns in Australia.

Tom, when he had the chance, often watched the bowling matches between clubs. It was compulsory to be dressed in appropriate garments before players were allowed on the green, so it was quite a pleasant sight to watch the bowlers dressed all in white, with their straw hats on. The greens were always in perfect order.

From Fremantle the ship went to Adelaide, discharging cargo there, then moving on to Melbourne, another magnificent city. The streets were wide and the business buildings impressive, but Tom felt that he wouldn't like to drive a car in an Australian city, for a pedestrian on a legal crossing stood a very good chance of never reaching the other side of the road. Australia is a motorist's country, like the United States.

From Melbourne the next port would be Sydney, New South Wales, the first part of Australia to be colonised. Botany Bay is close by, and everybody knows who were settled there in the early nineteenth century. Sydney is a magnificent city, and Tom took it to be the oldest. It seemed to be the landing point of all emigrants, as larger passenger ships of all nationalities discharged their living cargo at this port. In fact, Tom saw such ships himself as they docked not far from where his ship was lying, just round the corner from the famous bridge.

Tom had a relation living in Sydney, so he was able to visit him on occasions.

The next port would be Newcastle, and by the names of the local suburbs one would think he was back on Tyneside. This was a strongly indus-trialised area, with coalmining close by, suggesting that stalwarts from the north-east of England had settled there originally. The River Hunter, on which this area stands, was discovered by a Naval officer in charge of a boat's crew when searching for escaped convicts. The entrance was not visible from the seaward side. Probably that is the corner where Mr Micawber turned when he eventually made good by becoming mayor of a small settlement.

Newcastle was well protected from winds off the sea, which could blow very hard at times. The main street ran parallel with the river, and was very attractive, with good shops, all very clean, while the street led right down to the beach, which attracted many holidaymakers. Many times

Tom walked this street, and admired the shops, with their varied goods for sale.

The next port would be Brisbane, another port tucked away up a river, which was entered around a large bluff. Some said this was Australia's largest city, as it was spread out over many square miles, but nothing was concentrated in any particular area. Now this was the last port up the coast, and discharging was completed. The ship now commenced loading, retracing her direction to the same ports again, and by the time she reached Fremantle she was loaded for home ports.

On one voyage they went to a small port called Wallaroo, up the Spencer Gulf, and loaded five thousand tons of barley in bags and then back to Sydney to load the upper decks.

Tom remembers Wallaroo because he entertained the mayor, with his officers and their ladies, to dinner one night, and a very nice occasion it was, too. This town was built originally around copper mines, and there was a plaque indicating where the last mine was worked, and the date when it closed — 1923.

It was here that Tom saw a most unusual sight while walking around the residential area. He came across a house with very tall fencing, which made him curious, and on looking over he saw between forty and fifty baby kangaroos, about one year old, leaping around all over the place. He found out that the man who lived in the house bought the baby kangaroos from hunters who had shot the mothers carrying these babies in their pouches. He worked up a business exporting them to circuses and zoos.

On making inquiries as to why the kangaroos did not escape from this small enclosure by jumping over the fencing, he was told that the animals did not have sufficient space to make a run, which they needed to do to give them the power to jump so high. Well, thought Tom, some people make a living in strange sorts of ways. By the look of so many of these small kangaroos they would take a lot of looking after to keep them healthy, and the food bill would be rather costly.

Now it came to Tom's last voyage in the *Mystic*, although he didn't know that until he arrived back in Manchester. He had a month's leave, and returned to the ship, which was loading in Rotterdam for New Zealand. The ship was loaded at Continental ports, loading being completed at Le Havre. She left Le Havre on 21 December 1962 for Auckland, Wellington, and the Bluff.

On 24 December Tom became sixty-four years old.

They sailed to transit the Panama Canal, and the weather was unusually rough until they reached the north-east trade winds, after which it was fairly good for the rest of the way. Taking oil fuel at Curaçao she proceeded on to the Canal.

The voyage across the South Pacific was on the same pattern as previous voyages. On completing discharging in New Zealand, the ship had to load at Australian ports for the United Kingdom, the first port being Newcastle, New South Wales. The Queen and the Duke of Edinburgh were visiting Australia on the Royal Yacht *Britannia* about February 1963 and Captain Tom's ship was leaving Newcastle on the day the *Britannia* was arriving at Sydney.

He was bound for Sydney, too, which is only four hours' run from Newcastle. He was told not to arrive before 11 a.m. as the *Britannia* with the Queen and the Duke aboard was arriving at 10 a.m. The weather was really dirty when Tom arrived and the pilot could not board until inside the Heads. As the *Mystic* passed into her berth, the *Britannia* could be seen at the passenger wharf and the Royal couple meeting the dignitaries of Australia. She received a great welcome from the Australian people.

After three days or so the Royal party left on the *Britannia* and Tom went down to see the crowds. He positioned himself on the upper floor of the Customs shed, and could look right down on the deck of the *Britannia*.

In time the Queen and the Duke arrived and said goodbye to the dignitaries and so went on board, with the band playing the National Anthem. The *Britannia* prepared to leave, and just as she started to move slowly out the Queen and the Duke came out on deck and waved to

The author,
Captain R. C. Proctor OBE, relaxing in his twilight years.

everyone. Most of the people around Tom had tears running down their faces as they waved back to the Royal party, which impressed Tom very much.

After leaving Sydney the *Mystic* called at Melbourne, Adelaide, Albany and Fremantle. At the latter place the *Britannia* was tied up to the dock and the *Mystic* berthed close astern of her. The Royal party were not on board this time, as they were still on tour in Australia, eventually returning home by plane. The *Britannia* was paying an official visit to the port and left the day before the *Mystic*, which left Fremantle fully loaded for Manchester and other UK ports. They arrived in Manchester in May and Tom was told he would be relieved of his command after all the cargo had been discharged. It was 29 May 1963 when he eventually handed the ship over to another Master.

Captain Tom Sloane had about three months' leave to work off. When he had taken that, with only about two months left in the year he relieved on two ships on coastal work. It came to the end of the year and Tom's sixty-fifth birthday, and after having lunch with the directors at the London office he went into retirement. He had been with his company fifty years, a period he can look back on without any regrets.

He was still well and hearty and now he was going to make the best of his retirement. His wife and family were pleased to have Tom with them in one piece, as he had been through two long wars which did not spare the seafarer. He had been to most of the countries on the trading routes of the world, sometimes away from home for two years at a time, so he felt a little restless for the first year or two through being in one port so long.

His home is only a few minutes' walk from the sea, and he sees the ships at anchor at the bottom of the road when waiting to enter the river, and he feels as if he were aboard himself. Storms often occur on this windy north-east coast, bringing the smack of salt water into his face. Tom feels happy and secure in his home, but does not mind bracing up to the wind now and again just to stir his circulation.

It is a long stretch back to the time when as a boy apprentice he threw his bag over the gunwale and started his career on his first ship, *Tuscan Prince*, in the river Tyne, bound for Antwerp, London and the Plate. And now, as this story ends, Captain Tom Sloane says, 'Goodbye and pleasant sailing.'

The ships Tom sailed on

	Name	Year Built	Gross Tons	Remarks
1.	*Tuscan Prince*	1913	5284	Wrecked 14/9/39
2.	*Portuguese Prince*	1912	4981	Broken up 1934
3.	*Ocean Prince*	1907	5101	Wrecked 1916
4.	*Asiatic Prince*	1910	2889	Torp. 305/18
5.	*Merchant Prince*	1902	3092	Sold 1927
6.	*Arabian Prince*	1919	5764	Sold 1927
7.	*Algerian Prince*	1919	3089	Sold 1936
8.	*Cyprian Prince*	1919	3071	Sold 1936
9.	*Siberian Prince*	1915	5604	Sold 1933
10.	*African Prince*	1917	5119	Sold 1939
11.	*Egyptian Prince*	1922	3490	Sold 1946
12.	*Javanese Prince*	1926	8587	Torp. 1941
13.	*Stuart Prince*	1905	4129	Sold 1935
14.	*Corsican Prince*	1922	3493	Sold 1938
15.	*Sicilian Prince*	1922	3489	Sold 1946
16.	*Syrian Prince*	1936	3072	Sold 1954
17.	*Tudor Prince*	1940	3994	Sold 1957
18.	*Indian Prince*	1926	8587	Sunk 1943
19.	*Highland Prince*	1942	7043	Sold 1955
20.	*Welsh Prince*	1944	7381	Sold 1954
21.	*Atchison Victory*	Ex. US Marine		
22.	*Scottish Prince*	1942	7081	Sold 1955
23.	*British Prince*	Ex. US Marine		Sold 1955
24.	*Cingalese Prince*	1950	8827	Sold 1964
25.	*Edenmore*	1958	15,000DW	Ore Carrier
26.	*Javanese Prince II*	1944	8827	Sold 1961
27.	*Eastern Prince*	1950	8827	Sold 1964
28.	*Mystic*	1959	7600	